TALES
FROM
THE
DERRICK
FLOOR

TALES FROM THE DERRICK FLOOR

A PEOPLE'S HISTORY OF THE OIL INDUSTRY

MODY C. BOATRIGHT AND WILLIAM A. OWENS

DOUBLEDAY & COMPANY, INC.

GARDEN CITY, NEW YORK

1970

Library of Congress Catalog Card Number 75–111284

Copyright © 1970 by Mody C. Boatright and William A. Owens

All Rights Reserved

Printed in the United States of America

First Edition

To the men and women
who made the American oil industry
this book
is respectfully dedicated

ACKNOWLEDGMENTS

This book is a by-product of the Oral History of Texas Oil Pioneers, a project sponsored by the University of Texas and supported by the generosity of the late Mrs. Walter B. Sharp of Houston and her friends. Begun in 1952, the project aimed at getting on tape the memoirs of as many of the founders of the industry as possible. The authors of this book were the directors of the project and personally conducted most of the interviews.

Since 1952, several hundred persons have been interviewed. From these, more than a hundred were selected to record their histories in more than two hundred hours of tape. These persons represent all types of persons in any way connected with the development of the Texas oil fields. Their total experience reaches out to cover fields in Pennsylvania, West Virginia, Oklahoma, California, Arkansas, Louisiana, Burma, India, Russia, and Mexico.

Special appreciation is due these men and women for what is essentially their life stories. Without the interest and financial aid of Mrs. Sharp the book would not have been possible. Miss Winnie Allen, former Archivist of the University of Texas, was responsible for the organization and supervision of the Oral History project. To her we owe much. There are others too numerous to mention to whom we express our appreciation for aids of many kinds.

CONTENTS

AROUND

THE

HEADACHE

POST: AN

INTRODUCTION

Every business needs a headache post. The oil business has one—invented, built, named by roughnecks who were cracked on the head by a walking beam. Bert Stivers, who started roughnecking in 1903, gives the reason:

> The headache post is six by eight and it's about ten feet long. And it sets upright on the derrick floor on the main sill of the rig and goes up and when the beam is working and at its longer stroke, it misses the top of that headache post about four to six inches. So if anything . . . would break, that beam wouldn't fall in the derrick but would fall down and hit that headache post and stop it. That's what would keep it from falling on you when you was there at the throttle running the engine.

The headache post was a fact. It was also a device and a symbol. It was good to hold onto when things were going cussing wrong, a good prop to lean against when the rig was shut down and a man could sit long enough to catch his breath and spin a yarn. In the early days, the derrick floor was at the center of oil-field life—of the work, the tales, the jokes they played on one another.

"Hey, Boll Weevil, you go over to that rig and borrow me some skyhooks," a driller would yell.

If the boll weevil went, and came back to hear himself laughed at, and stayed on to work knowing it would take a long time to live the kidding down, he became a part of the oil fields, and a part of a history that had its beginnings in the tales told around the derrick floor.

Theirs is not a history told in days and months and years—not with exactness of time and place and people. It is a history told with another kind of authenticity, the authenticity that comes from being there, from seeing the events as they happened—more important, from being actors in the developing drama.

Such a history defies chronological telling. Not that major events cannot be documented. They can—in countless newspaper reports, in technical records of wells and fields and production, in leases, deeds, and abstracts. These are the facts that slip out of the mind. What remains is the scene—the dramatic moment of the gusher coming in, the blowout, the fire in well or earthen lake. From field to field, from person to person, the experiences are remarkably similar, and themes begin to shape the pattern of telling.

This history, then, is that of some one hundred people from the oil fields—drillers, lease hounds, roughnecks, boardinghouse keepers, policemen, lawyers—telling what it was like to be there. Some faithfulness to their recurring themes has been attempted. In the excitement of recalling and telling, however, there is frequent spilling over from one to another, as in the fields many things were happening at once.

There is a difference between telling a story on a derrick floor and telling it into the microphone of a tape recorder. Some of the flavor of language and inflection has to be lost. No matter how much is lost, however, enough remains to make the story full and strong. Reading it, one can truthfully say that this is the first American industry to write its own history.

TALES

FROM

THE

DERRICK

FLOOR

. . . only thing is, when the oil bug bites you, why, you stick by it harder and closer.

—V. B. Daniels, after forty-nine years in the Sour Lake field

The oil business as you may understand is filled with miracles that we never get through talking about or telling stories. And when you get through, even the professional liar couldn't misrepresent things too badly because these miracles still happen.

—Fain Gillock, wildcatter and spokesman for the industry

ONE

HUNDRED

YEARS

OF

AMERICAN

OIL

1

I. The petroleum industry celebrated its hundredth anniversary in
1959. This was an appropriate date, since the first well drilled specifically for oil was completed in 1859. On Saturday, August 27,
1859, "Uncle Billy" Smith, who had been employed by Edwin L.
Drake to drill a well near Titusville, Pennsylvania, noted that his
drill stem had dropped into a crevice at a depth of 69½ feet. He with-
drew his tools, meaning to resume work on Monday. On Sunday
afternoon he looked into the well and saw that oil had risen almost
to the surface. He bailed out a quantity and rushed to Titusville to
spread the news.

If this event marked the beginning of the oil industry, it was also the culmination of a series of events extending over several decades. For the Pennsylvania Rock Oil Company would not have been organized and the Drake well would not have been drilled if at least some of the commercial possibilities of petroleum had not been known. Man's knowledge of the existence of petroleum no doubt antedates recorded history. Oil springs in what is now the United States had been noted from the sixteenth century onward, and the American Indians were known to have used asphalt from oil deposits as calking for their canoes and liquid oil as a medicine. Since faith in Indian remedies was strong in the nineteenth century, it is not surprising that before 1850 enterprising men began bottling "Rock" oil or "Seneca" oil for sale as a medicine. But it became apparent that only a small fraction of the oil available could be marketed in this manner. For the supply was being rapidly increased by the accidental discovery of oil in wells being drilled in Pennsylvania, West Virginia, and Kentucky to tap underground deposits of brine to be evaporated and refined into salt.

The search for a wider market turned attention to petroleum as the source of a much needed illuminant. As early as 1819, crude oil had been burned to produce light, but the resulting smoke and odor precluded its wide use. James Young in Scotland had in 1847 produced a salable lamp oil from petroleum from an oil spring encountered in a coal mine. This supply, however, was soon exhausted, and he turned to shale. His process was exported to the United States and Canada. Research was undertaken to determine whether petroleum could supply a competitive and perhaps superior product. Several chemists, the most influential of whom was Benjamin Silliman, professor of chemistry at Yale University, made analyses of the oil and reported favorably upon its possibilities as a source of both lubricants and illuminants. Samuel Kier, famous for his hardly profitable venture into the marketing of petroleum as a medicine, is given credit for setting up the first refinery. It was located in Pittsburgh and its daily capacity never exceeded five barrels. Chemists found ways to reduce the odor and in other ways improve the product of his still, and more efficient lamps were designed. The salt drillers had not only found oil for the chemists to convert into useful products; they had also developed steam-powered equipment for sinking wells.

The time was ripe in 1855 for the organization of the first oil company. This was the Pennsylvania Rock Oil Company, which, after reorganization, employed Edwin Drake to supervise the development of its properties on Oil Creek.

The boom that followed Drake's success presented many problems—technical, social, and legal—whose solution required ingenuity and time. There was a frenzy of leasing and drilling. Within ten years the industry had spread down Oil Creek Valley to its confluence with the Allegheny River at Oil City and along the Allegheny Valley from Franklin to Warren. There was production also in West Virginia, Kentucky, and Ohio. Production was unregulated and would remain so until the fourth decade of the next century— and a thousand wells were drilled where hundreds would have recovered the oil with less waste. Periods of overproduction drove prices down. The influx of workers and camp followers created such prototypical boom towns as Pithole, which had not existed as a town before the discovery of oil in January 1865, but which by May of the same year had an estimated population of fifteen thousand, a considerable number of whom were criminals.

Storage and transportation problems were acute. Coopers could not make barrels fast enough. Thousands of teamsters moved their wagons over quagmire roads. Barrels were rafted down Oil Creek on freshets created by opening dams above. Railroads extended spurs into the oil fields, hauling oil first in barrels, then in wooden tanks mounted on flatcars, and finally in horizontal steel cylinders mounted on wheels. Oil began flowing through the first pipe line— five miles long—in 1865. By 1874, a sixty-mile line carried 7500 barrels of oil to Pittsburgh daily, and in 1879, a 110-mile line led from Bradford to Williamsport, Pennsylvania. The first ship to carry oil across the Atlantic made the trip in 1864, with its cargo in barrels.

By 1870, the steamer *Charles* had been fitted with fifty-nine steel tanks with a total capacity of 794 tons. In 1886, the first vessel designed specifically as a tanker was launched.

Samuel Kier's tiny still was made obsolete in 1861 when a plant began operation in Oil Creek. Soon the refinery typically would make its appearance wherever oil in quantity was discovered. Although in some localities shallow wells were put down with spring-pole equipment powered by human muscle, the basic machine remained the salt driller's steam-powered percussion drill, known as the standard rig. Derricks became taller, the engines more powerful, drill stems and bits heavier. Various special tools were designed for such jobs as reaming and recovering objects lost in the well. The improved tools and techniques permitted drilling to depths of a thousand feet or more.

Exploration continued, and by the end of the century oil was being produced commercially in thirteen states, with Ohio, West Virginia, and Pennsylvania accounting for more than sixty per cent of the nation's total.*

As new fields were discovered the output of the wells often exceeded the capacity of storage, transportation, and refining facilities, and the price of crude oil fell below the cost of production. As early as 1862 a young produce commission merchant of Cleveland had given financial backing to Samuel Andrews to go into the business of refining. The business prospered, and it led to further investments and the organization of the Standard Oil Company in 1870. Rockefeller and his associates saw the chaotic condition of the industry as an opportunity. By advantageous contracts with the railroads and by control of the pipe lines, the company was able by 1879 to market about ninety-five per cent of the nation's refined oil. It developed an efficient system of retailing, first by establishing

* Production figures in barrels for 1901 are given below:

Ohio	26,648,000	Indiana	5,757,000	Kansas	179,000
West Virginia	14,177,000	Texas	4,394,000	Kentucky	127,000
Pennsylvania	12,625,000	New York	1,207,000	Oklahoma	7,000
California	8,787,000	Colorado	461,000	Wyoming	5,000

bulk stations in the towns and cities, and then by packing kerosene in five-gallon cans sold through grocery stores.

In 1892 a suit was filed against the Standard Oil Trust under the recently passed Sherman Anti-Trust Act. After long litigation a decree of the Supreme Court in 1911 ordered the dissolution of the trust and the breaking up of the huge corporation into thirty-eight separate companies. By that time its monopoly was being threatened by growing independent companies that had their origin at Spindletop.

II. The coming in of the Lucas Gusher on a low mound near Beaumont, Texas, on January 10, 1901, has justly been called the most important event in the history of the oil industry since Drake's discovery forty-two years earlier. It was a signal for four decades of expansion rivaled only by the automobile and steel industries, to which it was related. It and the other discoveries that followed it, as has been suggested, resulted in the formation of strong independent companies able to compete with Standard Oil.

The Lucas Gusher was drilled with rotary equipment after the standard rig had failed. Although the rotary was manufactured in Corsicana and was used in that field, it was little known outside the immediate vicinity before Spindletop. The introduction of the Hughes roller rock bit in 1909 would greatly extend its use and reduce the unit cost of drilling. The Lucas Gusher also revealed a geological formation hitherto unexplored for oil. Other salt domes under mounds visible on the surface would be quickly explored, and after the introduction of the torsion balance and the seismograph in the 1920s, other domes not apparent from surface indications would be found.

The Spindletop discovery brought about a revolution in fuel. Gas (more often artificial than natural) and electricity were becoming increasingly available to town and city dwellers, foretelling a shrinking market for kerosene. But even the previous market could not have absorbed the great quantities of oil flowing from the Texas coastal plain. The producers turned to fuel oil for steam engines. It was determined that three barrels of oil would produce as much energy as a ton of coal. With a plentiful supply of petroleum in sight, sugar refineries, electric generating plants, railroads, steamship lines, and the United States Navy could confidently convert to oil. Carl Coke Rister in *Oil Titan of the Southwest* quotes an observer as writing, "Within a year of its [Spindletop's] discovery, Beaumont oil is burning in Germany, England, Cuba, Mexico, New York, and Philadelphia. By its energy steamers are being propelled across the ocean, trains are hastening across the continent, electricity generated and artificial ice frozen in New York, ores ground and stamped in Mexico, Portland cement manufactured in Havana and Texas, and gas enriched in Philadelphia; and this too, while half the world is either unaware or incredulous of the value of this fuel."

Finally, the discovery came on the eve of the automobile age. In 1895, there were five cars and no trucks registered in the United States. In 1901, the number would be 619,500 passenger cars and 20,000 trucks, and the sales of gasoline, a drug on the market in the nineteenth century, would exceed the sales of kerosene. As late as 1908, tankers bringing crude oil from Beaumont, Texas, to refineries in Bayonne, New Jersey, loaded on excess gasoline and dumped it far out in the Atlantic.

The history of Spindletop may well begin with Pattillo Higgins, a citizen of Beaumont, who became convinced that oil or gas could be found by drilling near a gas seep on Sour Springs mound (later called Spindletop), and that the cheap fuel he hoped to find could be made the basis of an industrial city. He succeeded in interesting local capital and in 1892 organized the Gladys City Oil, Gas, and Manufacturing Company. Three attempts to drill failed, and the company's funds were exhausted. A trade was made with A. E. Lucas, whose first attempt failed and left him also without funds. He secured the backing of Guffey and Galey, Pennsylvania oilmen who had operated at Corsicana; and Galey, for whom they had drilled in that field, recommended to Lucas that the drilling contract be let to the Hamill brothers. They succeeded in sinking a well through 285 feet of quicksand that had baffled all previous attempts, and they saw oil gushing from the well at a rate estimated at 75,000 to 100,000 barrels, a sight that had never been seen in the world before.

Following Spindletop came four decades of growth to which such Hollywoodish adjectives as "fabulous," "tremendous," and "marvelous" may appropriately be applied. Other oil-bearing salt domes were found along the coastal plain, and simultaneous probing in Oklahoma and California opened up other great provinces. The center of the industry shifted to the West and Southwest. In 1907, California took the lead in oil production. In 1914, it was surpassed by Oklahoma. These states maintained a race for first place until 1928, when Texas took the lead, which it has since maintained. By 1940, many other provinces had been discovered and oil was being produced in twenty-four states. In addition, American oil companies had millions invested in foreign countries, including Venezuela and the Near Eastern states.

During this period there were significant changes in the tools of production. The rotary rig became the basic drilling equipment, but would hardly be recognizable to one who had seen only the rig used to drill the Lucas Gusher. The operators, though still called roughnecks, were highly skilled technicians who were informed about what was going on under the ground by dials and gauges. Improved metallurgy made possible a drilling pipe with the weight-sustaining capacity required for drilling five miles in the earth. Drilling fluids, still called mud, were scientifically mixed to meet local requirements. Equipment was designed for directional drilling, so it was possible to drill under public buildings and to drill several wells from a single location, especially desirable for off-shore exploration. There was increasing specialization, with firms limiting their activities to a single service, such as fire-fighting, acidizing, and cementing.

Petroleum geology, generally held in contempt by oilmen before 1901, became, along with geophysics, the chief means of locating reserves. By 1920, the major oil companies had established geological departments and were relying on them to find favorable structures. Petroleum engineering became a profession, and courses in this field were introduced in the leading universities. Refining reached the creative stage. The first refineries were little more than distilleries in which heat was applied to crude petroleum and the components were separated in the order of their boiling points. The first major change came in 1913 with the use of the Burton thermal cracking process, which greatly increased the gasoline yield by breaking larger molecules into smaller ones. The anti-knock properties of tetraethyl lead were discovered in 1921. The time would soon come when gasoline and fuel oils would be put together according to predetermined specifications.

More significant was the development of conservation techniques which made possible the recovery of billions of barrels of oil that under earlier methods of production would have been left in the earth. The legal foundations for prorated production were laid in 1900, when the Supreme Court established the doctrine of "correlative rights," which meant in effect that a landowner was bound to respect the rights of others whose oil came from the same source. Oklahoma and Texas passed proration laws in 1915 and 1919 respectively, but proration was not generally effective until the 1930s. The governors of several oil-producing states met in 1929 to work out a program. When in 1931 the enormous production from the East Texas and Oklahoma City fields flooded the market and drove the price of crude oil down to a few cents a barrel, the governors of Texas and Oklahoma called out the National Guard to enforce shutdown orders. The National Recovery Act of 1933 provided for the regulation of the oil industry, until the Act was struck down by the Supreme Court in 1935. In that same year Congress passed the Connally "Hot Oil" Bill, which prohibited the shipment in interstate commerce of oil produced in violation of state law. Congress later enacted the Interstate Oil Compact Act, under which member states assumed the obligation to enact and enforce laws to lessen the waste of oil and gas. The high court eventually held that a legitimate means of preventing waste was to limit production to market demand. The objects of the laws now in effect in the major oil-producing states have been summarized by J. Stanley Clark (in the *American Petroleum Quarterly*, Centennial Edition) as follows:

> To protect and increase the ultimate recovery of the nation's oil reserves, and
> To safeguard the property rights of every landowner in a pool.
> To prevent production in excess of what is called Maximum Efficient Rate, these working measures were set up:
> The unitization of pools, so that production is allocated fairly among the different property owners;
> The proper spacing of wells and provision for their even flow, and
> The establishment of monthly "allowables," based on the monthly market demand forecast posted by the Federal Bureau of Mines.

With the development of a scientific technology for efficient production and with the establishment of legal machinery for maintaining conservation and stabilization, the oil industry had by 1940 reached maturity.

•

III. The year 1940 also marks the beginning of a five-year period of unprecedented expansion, during which petroleum was put to a variety of new uses. It was in 1940 that President Roosevelt proclaimed the United States the arsenal of freedom, and asked the oil industry to develop fuel for the planes that were to be produced at the rate of 50,000 a year. The annual production of crude oil in the United States in 1941 was 1,400,000,000 barrels; in 1945, it was 1,700,000,000 barrels. When the war began, American refineries were turning out 40,000 barrels of high-octane aviation gasoline a year; in 1945, the figure was 514,000 barrels. By August 1942, 9,000,000,000 gallons of gasoline were being delivered to the army a day, and during a seven-week period during the summer of 1944 the fleet consumed 15,000,000 barrels of fuel oil. Coastal tankers suffered heavy losses from German submarines, and to meet the demands for transportation, pipe line mileage was increased from 127,351 in 1941 to 142,000 in 1945. Notable achievements were the laying, with government subsidies, of the Big Inch and Little Inch pipe lines, the former a 24-inch line carrying crude oil from Longview, Texas, to Norris City, Illinois, and later to New York, and the latter a 20-inch line carrying refined products from Houston to Linden, New Jersey.

If, as Viscount Curzon said in 1918, "The Allies floated to victory on a wave of oil," that wave was a small one in comparison to that in the 1940s.

The war also hastened the development of the petrochemical industry. In 1937, only one oil company was producing petrochemicals. In 1957, sixty-six companies were so engaged. Synthetic rubber was being made on a small scale before the war, but it was not until the supply of natural rubber was cut off that a large industry developed and made the United States self-sufficient. Similarly, the cutting off of the foreign supply of vegetable oil revolutionized the manufacture of household cleaners and paints and varnishes. Products continue to multiply. Today one could count more than two thousand common articles derived from petroleum. They would include roofing, floor covering, combs, brushes, garden hoses, several kinds of fabrics, containers, insecticides, medicinal alcohol, and so on.

The question of whether or not the oil reserves of the United States can sustain the ever increasing consumption of petroleum products has frequently been raised. The greatest known reserves lie outside the country, particularly in Venezuela and the Near Eastern states, and American companies with holdings in these regions, where costs of production are lower than in the United States, import a considerable quantity of oil. The search for new fields in the United States continues. Exploration of the continental shelf is in its infancy. Several years ago, the oil geologist Everette DeGolyer said that if salt domes were as prevalent off shore as on shore, ten and a half billion barrels of oil should be recovered off the coasts of Louisiana and Texas alone. And the Bureau of Mines has estimated that the shale deposits in Colorado, Utah, and Wyoming would yield five hundred billion barrels of oil. The techniques for utilizing this source are known, though at present costs are too high to compete with liquid petroleum. At present, oil companies are expending nearly a billion dollars a year for production and exploration. New electronic oil-finding devices are in the experimental stages, and new discoveries are anticipated. The northern Alaskan field promises to be the largest ever discovered. The immediate problem is not the scarcity of reserves, but the pollution of the air by the internal combustion engine. If this problem is solved, petroleum will be our chief source of energy for a long time.

FINDING

OIL

2

The search for petroleum began where there was plain evidence of its existence: at oil springs, gas seeps, and slicks in low places or along creek banks; or where oil or gas was encountered in wells drilled for water or salt. From successes in these locations, exploration spread until the limits of the fields were established. New fields were sought on terrain similar to that of producing fields. Both scientific and pseudoscientific methods of finding oil grew out of observations of surface manifestations.

As early as 1842, Sir William Logan, director of the Geological Survey of Canada, noted that a series of oil seepages occurred along an anticline paralleling the St. Lawrence River. In 1860, Henry D.

Rogers of the University of Glasgow read a paper on the concurrence of oil and anticlines. He knew the location of the Drake well, but had not seen it. Two significant events occurred in 1861. T. Sterry Hunt published an article in the Montreal *Gazette* in which he formulated the theory of the accumulation of oil in geological traps, and E. B. Andrews traced a line of uplift from Washington County, Ohio, to a point beyond oil wells on the Little Kanawha River, and noted the presence of oil wells and springs. Two years later Rogers stated without qualification that in the United States oil was found only on anticlines.

The first professional petroleum geologist is said to be I. C. White, who resigned from the Geological Survey in 1875 to become a consulting geologist. He could confidently take this step. He had traced the oil-bearing formation of Pennsylvania into West Virginia, and after unsuccessful attempts to interest oilmen, he drilled at his own expense and thus made himself financially independent and established his professional qualifications. He said that while all the great oil and gas wells in the United States were on anticlines, not all anticlines produced oil. For the rest of the century, in so far as geology was employed in oil exploration, its effort was to locate on closed anticlines. Other traps, such as salt domes, faults, and stratigraphic traps, remained unknown and unsought until 1901.

Oilmen, however, paid little attention to the academic geologists. They were largely ignorant of their writings and would have been inclined to be skeptical of their theories even if they had known them. The circumstance that the first oil fields were along streams led to the search along other streams. Practical oilmen examined surface rocks and cuttings from producing wells and thus collected a fund of information that went by the name of "creekology."

In the meantime, knowledge of subsurface geology was accumulating with each well that was drilled; and with the advent of the torsion balance, the gravity meter, and the seismograph, it was possible to map structures that no drill had ever pierced. By 1920, the

major oil companies had departments of geology, whose work greatly
reduced the number of failures.

Before scientific exploration took over, however, there was a
long period of the pseudoscientific and of the plain superstitious.
Wildcatters then hunted for oil—and still do to a lesser extent—
with the help of persons who leaned to some degree on the occult.
The old divining rod, or "wiggle stick," usually a forked limb, used in
search for water and minerals was applied to oil. From this, the more
enterprising developed new devices, "doodlebugs" of various de-
signs, some purportedly electrical, some chemical, some complicated
enough to have interchangeable vials of oil and metals. Clairvoy-
ants, fortunetellers, and spiritualists did a thriving business through
the 1920s. By chance or whatever, they hit often enough for their
successes to become part of a ragged legend.

In the feverish hunt for the exact location for the lucky strike,
the wildcatter was likely to rely on a strange mixture of surface observation, superstition, the occult, and even the divine. In some ways
he was as well off as the man who depended on a geologist. Even
today only about 15.5 per cent of the wells drilled in rank wildcat
locations are producers. As John Galey said seventy years ago, the
only geologist (or diviner) who can tell with certainty whether oil
will be found is Dr. Drill.

Proving Spindletop

That was way over here where we had the five wells. No, just
say one little space between two, and here there was three. Then
there was three—no, two—that made the five springs and that's what
they had. And the water in them was a little bit different from
others. Wasn't the same kind of water. Now I worked out what
caused that. There was more gas coming through one of them than
either one of the other four. And the more gas, the more mineral
would come off from the gas coming out. The gas brought some
minerals up—that wet gas, you know—and it made its deposits.
Now I went back there to this one where I got my gas in the can.

Just a couple of men down in the hole—went down on a ladder only
about eight foot down. And they took the two kerosene-oil cans,
five-gallon cans, and a little piece of rubber hose about a foot long
or something like that. I connected them together—they both had
spouts where they could pour—and a little valve to close it or open
it.

Well, I packed all around the water at the bottom, so the gas
had to come up through the can. Now that gas would open it up. I
could hear the old can pop and make a noise, a tin noise. Well, now,
when it filled up, I turned the little valve and cut it off so as it
couldn't come out. Now I took that can, when I caught the gas,
home with me. I showed it to my mother, my sister, and I took it to
Mr. Carroll's house and showed it to him. I burned it at night, a
pretty blue-red colored blaze at night.

—*Pattillo Higgins*

Creekology

For example, the old operator and developer of oil, he didn't
believe in geology. He figured out theories of his own. He believed
in creekology or something else. . . .

Well, it's explained in this way. A number of the fields in that
early date were found along creeks. And the reason of that was that
if at some time you had had an uplift or a swelling of the earth's
formations which produced and made an anticline, it would crack
the surface soils and a creek would develop—a stream would develop. So that was the reason for calling it creekology.

—*Fain Gillock*

Oil Smeller

We had what we called the oil smellers and oil witches. An oil
smeller was a fellow that went around and had one of these mineral
rods, you know, and he claimed that this instrument, when he passed
over certain ground, that he could tell whether there was oil. And
that proved to be and was a sort of a joke and a laughing stock. And
then lots of them would say, "Well, now, about oil—" They had oil
indications on the land surface. I have known at the time where
there would be seeps of gas in this locality, and then they would
light it. Sometimes it would light, and most of the time it would

prove to be vegetable gas or something of that kind. But there was right smart of that at that time. Then as time went on, why, the seismograph and deep-gravity machine come into general use.

And the information I have from them is that they can tell you where the possibilities of oil, but they can't tell you that the oil is there. In other words, they can tell you where is the prospect—best prospect to spend your money, to chance it, to make a production of it.

—*James Donohoe*

Old-timers will recall that the oil country was infested with oil smellers. One prominent Texas preacher went so far as to allege that he had X-ray eyes. He was a dramatist of the very highest order. His acting was superb, he would hold his hands high over his head as though he was pointing to the heavenly bodies, and with closed eyes would majestically prance around—suddenly stop, shudder as though he had palsy, and in a stentorian voice would declare that he was on the edge of an oil creek that was narrow, about fifty feet wide, and the main oil river would be found in the immediate vicinity. He was the most impressive of all oil smellers I have ever met, and should have quit the oil-smelling business and gone on the stage.

All he had to sell was his ability to look down in the earth for several hundred or several thousand feet, and see the oil. For a fee he would tell you just where to go. While when a geologist or oil smeller can locate an oil creek fifty feet wide—why, I'm just reluctant to take his advice about finding oil.

Another oil smeller had a small black box, and a cone-shaped instrument which he alleged had been entrusted to him by a life prisoner in a Spanish dungeon. Believe it or not, this oil smeller had the financial support of a wealthy and prominent Dallas businessman. The Dallas man had his bank write our New York office about this highly secret finding machine. Ultimately, I received copies of the correspondence and was told that if I believed the instrument had any merit, to make a deal with the Dallas man. I devoted long hours to study geology, and could not become interested in a dungeon-made machine that could tell me within a few inches the depth of an oil river. The president of our company severely criti-

cized my determination not to deal with the Dallas man for the use
of his oil-finding machine. But my friend Colonel Payne stood firmly
behind my position. Later, to appease our president, I leased the
Dallas oil smeller 160 acres of fee land, offsetting producing wells,
and he drilled two dry holes on it.

—H. P. Nichols

Dr. Griffith, Wiggle-stick Man

Dr. Griffith of Houston had a contrivance that nobody else
could work but he could. He had little lugs that looked like the size
of a silver pencil and it had a plate that would fit the palate, the
roof of his mouth. And from each side of this plate that protruded
from the mouth were coiled, highly coiled, springs of six or eight
inches long, on the end of which had little silver looking plates that
he could take between his forefinger and thumb of each hand. Then
out of the bottom of this plate came his mouth. He would thread-
screw one of these little lugs marked silver, or gold, or iron, or oil, or
gas, or sulphur, and then he would walk. This would be pointing ver-
tically, and sometimes he would start and tremble and you'd see this
lug draw down toward the ground. There he'd make a mark. And
then he would go at right angles to what he said would find where
sands crossed one another. His idea of an oil field was a gridiron,
sands going east and west and sands going north and south.

His instrument impressed a lumberman named Mr. Burt, R. E.
Burt, who gave him a half interest in many of his properties, the oil
interests. He was a lumberman. And while the production was
brought in, particularly at Humble, Texas, on some of his property,
it wasn't the result of his instrument, but he made, checked every
location. Sometimes the company would move a location five or six
feet. And, of course, there were dry holes drilled too, in different
counties of the state of Texas, but both parties became very, very
wealthy.

Dr. Griffith died not many years ago, and I think he has a son-
in-law in Houston and maybe a son in Houston. And there was many
a wildcat projected on the result of locations he made with this contrivance or apparatus that he used. He used to go into people's of-
fices, and sometimes they would put a box of silver coins somewhere.
And the idea was, he could locate it. And his explanation was that it
was something in these lugs plus a magnetism of his—in his body—

some companion property of chemistry that made it possible for him to locate these things.

I can't say that I believed in it. I've walked with him many, many times and made locations for the Texas Company and had him check them. And sometimes if he didn't get a good well, he'd come out and locate the sand at the end of your pipe rack. Drill the hole there. And on the pipe rack was all the iron in the world, and it didn't affect it.

—Alexander Balfour Patterson

I couldn't tell you much about the workings of it [the wiggle stick]. He held one part of it in his mouth, if I remember right. And the other part he held in his hands. And when he got over oil, there was a little lever there that would turn around.

Another time I was with Dr. Griffith in the Markham Oil Field. I was gonna drill a well, and he had carried me out to a location that he was drilling out in the country, out in the wilds, which was a wildcat. And I told him I wanted to go by my well, by my location, and he could tell me whether there was any oil there or not. When we got there, he says, "I wouldn't drill here, but," he says, "if you'll drill over there on the other side of the fence, a hundred feet away over on that side of the fence, I believe I'll put a little money with you on it. Because," he says, "there's no oil here." Well, I went on and drilled the well anyhow. And it come in a nice oil well, not a big well, but two or three hundred barrels a day. So the Doctor could make mistakes all right, even with his scientific machinery.

—Curt G. Hamill

Gas Seep at Batson

Old Uncle Ben Jordan told me to hitch the big horse with the white star on its face to the stick-back buggy, and take this man to Batson—take him down to where we had seen the water boiling out of the ground, and I did that. It was either July or August, and pretty dry. There was a muddy hole there where the ground was low—a pond we called it. We drove up there, and I told him that I had seen the water go up two feet above the ground during a wet spell when it was raining. There was a persimmon tree. He taken and cut one of those down—it was about the size of a broom around and possibly four or five feet long—and peeled the bark off it, and it peeled off very slick.

He just kept jabbing that down in the ground where there was just a little bit of water, and it was muddy, very mucky on top, and working it along until we got it down about three and a half or four feet or a little deeper. I noticed when he got on the buggy at Saratoga he put in a can and a box of matches and things like that. Well, after he got this worked down as far, I guess, as he felt like he could, when he thought it was deep enough, he cut that can with a tin snips and taken the pliers and rolled it up to something like a pin-point opening. He taken some of this stiff mud and dabbed it all around it —made a little chimney, I call it—and then got to striking matches, and looking at it.

He called me. "I want you to come down here, and when I strike a match, you get down there and look at that close, and see if you see any flash of light." Well, I looked at it for quite a while, and I said, "No, sir, I don't see any light at all." Then he said, "Look close." Then I said, "I believe I did see just a little flash." Then he said, "Yes, that's right." He said, "I think so."

So he would put his finger over it; he did then, and did it several times, and when he taken his hand away immediately he had the light—a match already burning—and make a nice little flash. So I said, "Yes, I can see it."

—W. E. Cotton

A *Wildcatter's Way*

I haven't used any very scientific method. It's kind of a little geology and a little doodlebugology and a little common sense and a few things put together. And in reality I've done most of my own thinking along that line rather than taking other people's advice.

I've always believed that there would be a direct method of locating oil. And I think we're getting closer and closer to that all the time. And I have not scientifically but in a way have assisted in the development along that line. And while it's now very dependable it has some virtue, and I think before long it will be a positive proposition just like locating uranium with a Geiger counter. And I've had a lot of fun with it and I've had a lot of outdoor exercise and I've kept up my enthusiasm and good health. And I've made enough to buy the groceries. And what more do you want?

It's unexplainable. We just think that oil gives off a ray of some kind that affects certain chemicals and indicates the presence of hydrocarbons in the ground. We think oil is giving off a ray just like uranium is or like any other substance. I think everything is susceptible of being detected if you knew just what to do. I've seen so many changes in my lifetime that nothing startles me at all. And I don't dispute anybody's claims or anything because no one knows what might come about.

My real definition of a doodlebug is "A little instrument that goes up and down and around and around and makes you spend your money drilling holes in the ground." And the law of averages will finally hit you a pool of oil. But in reality I think that the term "doodlebug" is applied to all so-called methods of direct location of oil. It's in very bad repute with the real oil people, but I've never been ashamed of my work in it because I've gotten along fine and I've accomplished most of what I wanted to do in life. And particularly I've kept my health. And I think keeping up my enthusiasm has had a lot to do with keeping my health.

I use them [doodlebugs] a whole lot. There's just no way to describe them. There are dozens of them that work on the same principle, but to use one you've got to have a lot of common sense and some knowledge of oil to get any effective results. It's my theory that if you knew what to look for you could see an oil field on top of the ground. But we haven't reached that point yet. If we had the close observation of a Indian tracker, we could probably go out and locate an oil field just from the vegetation, the growth, and the shape of the earth. 'Cause if you'll go to any oil field you'll see that it differs a little bit from the surrounding territory. And I think maybe that we'll develop quite a little along that line.

The most effective geologist that I've ever dealt with was a one-armed quarter Indian, who perhaps worked out more producing areas in this country than all the rest of the fellows put together. And he did most of his geology by climbing up on windmills and studying the country—the surface of the country. His name was Richards. He was down here fooling around the country and he worked for me awhile. And his old maps that he made of this country show some thirty oil fields, or thirty oil pools, that have since been developed.

He was not a graduate geologist. He was not licensed. His work was all just observing the surface and the vegetation in the area. I remember he made the location for the Schott field, which has probably produced more oil per acre than any other spot in this part of the country. And I remember him saying, "Well, now, don't want to get too far up dip and get in the gas, too much gas. So I think we better move it 150 feet west." So he moved that location there and the well came in making about a hundred barrels of oil and about thirty million feet of gas. Perfect. He couldn't have picked it any better if you'd had it laying out on the ground for him.

—O. W. Killam

The Boy with X-ray Eyes

I am going to tell you how it happened. They claimed that I could see water under the ground. Well, I didn't know then; I thought maybe I could. It was a vision. But I couldn't really see it; it was a feeling. I just felt, and knew it was there. The spring—it would just be a vision to me.

I suppose I was something like nine or ten years old when I told my father about it, and he said, "Well, we'll try it. You show me where there is water." That was close to Sanderson, Texas. There wasn't any water in the country. I located a well and told them that somewhere about sixty feet deep. They got to sixty-two feet deep and got water.

I went out to north of Del Rio, Texas, one time for a fellow named Guy Strickler—located three wells for him. He got water in two—in one he did not get the water, but he had faith enough in me (he felt the hole was a little crooked and he missed it), and he put in a shock and got plenty of water.

I never did go by pay. I don't know—I just didn't want to do it. Someway or another. I know now why it was. I don't suppose, really, I was supposed to commercialize on it.

So I got to wanting to charge people for it. Well, my father made them. He charged, oh, about around five hundred dollars if he got water.

Well, I located a well in Uvalde in our place there—north of Uvalde for Lee Lanford—a fellow named Lee Lanford. It has been so long ago I have to think awhile before I can recall all of them.

The switch will work for me, yes. Get you a peach limb is mighty good—a clean kind of wood is better. Get you one that is limber and take the forking end up and take the other end and give a bend, so you can hold it in each hand and start walking. Pretty soon that thing will start down and you can't stop it. It'll go down on you. I never claimed to have done much with it [the divining rod].

They claimed I saw it, and they looked at my eyes, and they did comment that I had very sharp eyes. I don't know who started calling them X-ray eyes. Somebody in the newspapers. I read about it [the Lucas Gusher] in the papers. Well, they wanted to test to see if I could locate oil in there. So they buried a barrel of oil and a barrel of water out where I didn't know where it was, and took me out there. I did this at night. At night—the darker the night the better. Well, I located the barrel of oil and the barrel of water. They had them buried about six feet under the ground. So they started out ready to go—to move out there, and I went out there—wanted to get rich, and it wasn't fair. I didn't work but a week or ten days and it left me there.

I was very tall—very heavy about thirteen. I imagine I was about six feet or five-eleven. I believe I was in the sixth grade. My brother, my father, W. W. Collier, and a man named Wingate went to Spindletop.

There would be one of them around, and he would tell me, "Now don't talk to people; they are liable to draw you out." They would say, "We don't want you to tell them what we are doing."

I can remember the Lucas Gusher—big gusher—seeing the mounds around them, the ground all dark. They already had it shut in then. They were just small mounds. I suppose at the base they would be about from eight to ten or twelve feet in diameter and probably two feet high right in the center. They claimed that that was gas escaping and blowing the dirt or sand out and piling it over. I don't remember now, but seems to me that the geologists in that time made them drill there in these mounds where the gas was escaping.

I stayed in the McFadden Flats. It was rooms belonging to Mc-Fadden. They tell me they wanted to get in with somebody that had money, and we get in with him, and that is where he put us in. In Beaumont.

And then he had a ranch—a big farm, too—past the Lucas Gusher going out there, and we stayed out there some. I can remember them telling when the Lucas Gusher came in—it was a big ranch farm and they worked lots of Negroes—I can remember them talking about it when the gusher came in. They said, "Boy, we thought it had happened!" It was about two miles from the gusher, and they claimed the windows just rattled when the gusher started. The well was running wild there.

My brother wrote up the contract [with McFadden]. He was a lawyer. I don't know whether McFadden ever did anything about it or not. We were trying to locate where there was some oil, and he [McFadden] was going to get the land. But I guess he did not make the location enough that he got it. The best I recall the land was a mile long and a half mile wide or something like that, and they bought a strip about two or three hundred yards wide—the length of a mile; and the location I made was on—I have forgotten what direction—but was on one end of the land, and they wouldn't sign any contract either—the Uvalde Oil Company or something was the matter, and my brother wouldn't tell them where to drill; so they went ahead and drilled anyhow, but they drilled on the other end of this mile, and missed the oil.

My father said, "We'll take him home. I guess we ought not try to commercialize on it." So we come on back home.

Once in a while some old fellow comes around and tells me that he still believes in me. I tell him I can't tell him there is water; I'll go help him, if I can be of any help to him. I have helped some of them. I think that was the way it was intended to be.

Once in a while we'll be walking out in the woods, and I have told her [Mrs. Finley], "I think there is water here. It's shallow." I couldn't prove it, but get a feeling walking along.

If you have ever been out in the weeds on a cold frosty morning —if you noticed yourself—there will be a streak that wouldn't be any frost. Well, the water is shallow under there, and there is some heat or something rising up from the ground that melted that frost, and in some connection of what is arising there I have the gift of whatever it is that I can feel.

The last fellow I remember wanting to pay me—I got him a well and he wanted to pay me—and I told him, "No, I didn't want that." I believe that it was a gift that was given to me to give to other people—maybe it will come back if I don't charge.

—Guy Finley

Madame Virginia

Well, I'm a reader. I'm Madame Virginia. At present I work in Abilene. I've worked in Austin, I've worked in Houston, I've worked in Fort Worth, I've worked in Dallas, I've worked in Tyler and Wichita Falls and many towns in Texas.

The first to ever come to me was that my father had some cattle and I was walking up the trail, I remember very well, and it come to me that someone had stole some of his cattle. And I went and told him that I thought some of his cattle had been stole and he told me at that time if I told him any more yarns like that he'd whup me. But in three days after that, Mr. Fry, where the Fry oil field was, come over and told my father that there had been twenty-five or thirty Buckle-D cattle shipped out of Brownwood.

I've always known I could read. I can't see why other people can't.

The first I ever remember of locating anywhere was in Wichita Falls, and that was at the Burkburnett field. I had a hotel in Wichita Falls at that time. Was the Alpine Hotel. And I only taken in men and most of them was men that worked at the Burkburnett oil field. One day there was one of the oilmen come in for his mail. And I told him, and I'll never know how come me to say it to him, I said, "You haven't got any mail, but I think you're going to get a message that your son has his arm broke, and got it broke at a gate." Well, he asked me how come me to say that to him and I didn't know, 'cause I didn't want to get them started because people have worried me ever since I was a child and I got nothing out of it.

But in two hours he got the message that his son had his arm broke and got it broke at a gate. And then he got after me to locate him a well. And I went with him and located several wells. And they come in and they was very good. And then there was other oilmen that come to me at that time but I got nothing out of that. So I finally quit.

It just comes to me. It just comes to me. A reader has a seeing mind just like other people has seeing eyes. It taken me for years to learn this. And I can see better with my mind than I can see with my eyes. And if I'm talking to someone about a plot of land and they go to draw me a plot of their land, I stop them, because I can't see the same with my eyes as I see with my mind.

I can tell them how the land looks before I ever get on the land. We had an oil boom in Abilene and I had oilmen that come to me and they wanted me to invest in some land. But I told them that I was going to invest in East Texas because I thought there was a field coming in there. And he told, the gentleman I was talking to told me, said, "You've been right all the time, Madame, but you're wrong now." But I did invest in some land near Hawkins, between Hawkins and Red Springs. I bought a hundred and sixty acres of land and before I bought this land I could see an old schoolhouse and I could see some tall derricks and I bought this land sight unseen. So I visited the place, and there was the old schoolhouse and the land; the lay of the land looked just like it had come to me. So I kept this land for fourteen years and then there was a big oil well come in at Hawkins.

I'll go back and tell you this. I was working in Abilene in '26 and there was a man that was picking cotton at Tye and he come in for reading. His wife had been ill. And I told him I thought his wife was going to be all right, that he lived in a place where there was going to be an oil field. And I asked him where he lived and he said he lived at Tyler and I said, "No, you don't, because this is a real small town." And he said, "Well, I live at Hawkins." And I said, "There's going to be an oil field in Hawkins." And he had two little boys and they bought some lots in Hawkins. And now they have wells on those lots.

I have never got an oil well on my land yet, but they're very close to me. And sometime I hope I do. But I leased it. My land was the only land that wasn't leased during the time the well come in at Hawkins. And I got a good price out of my lease. I've saved it because I wanted to wait until the oil got closer to it.

Time is something I can't tell, not unless it comes to me. I had a lady that visited me that her father was seriously ill and she wanted, she asked me how long I thought he'd last, because he had cancer and he was suffering. And I told her that I thought he would die on Wednesday along about six o'clock, and on Wednesday he died.

There was Mrs. Cooper that lived at Anson, Texas, and they was wanting to buy a ranch. And I told her to buy it, that later there was going to be an oil field on it. And they did, and it was twenty years before the oil come in, but they have a big field at Anson. And I located the oil field at Baird, and one at Noodle, one at Merkel, and many little towns.

I can ride on a train, I can get on a train and ride over it in a train at night and I can tell you when I'm riding over an oil field.

—*Ruth Bryan*

Miss Annie Buchanan, Corsicana Clairvoyant

First well was Colonel Humphers', but Desenburg owned it. Desenburg owned that property and my brother-in-law Walt Beasley was buyin' it—and he lost his wife. He said, "Miz Annie, I believe I'll give this property back." I said, "Let me look at you and see will it do you any good to give it back." So I looked at his hand and I described the oil. I said, "Boy," I said, "keep it." I said, "It'll pay fo' itself, by this time in a year, or a year and a half." I said, "Here oil." He said, "I thought you had some sense. No such a thing as oil under the earth." I said, "All right, when you give it up it's goin' to be a white man comin' here and I'm goin' to tell him 'bout that oil."

So sho nuff, I told Mr. Humphers. I said, "Mr. Humphers," I said, "here's the first well. I told my brother-in-law 'bout this," I said. "You want me describe it to you," I said. I said, "Here's the first well." And so there's the first well right there. I tol' him 'bout it and he got the oil.

And not only that field I told. Right here in Corsicana I told 'em long time ago, go for oil right here in town, and they got that. They jus' keep on gettin' oil. Yes, suh. So many different places I told that they's got it—and never missin'. Down to Teague, Kosse, Carthage, Beaumont, Oklahoma—so many different places I told 'em.

Yes, suh, he [Mr. Humphers] give me eight thousand and five hundred dollars. Yes, suh. Eight thousand and five hundred dollars. Mr. Humphers—he's gone in now. Paid for this home—put up this home. And he told me, he said, "Annie," he said, "on this place I'll see you. It will be nice to you. You'll be here in Corsicana." He say, "I want you to stay here the longest day as you live." And I told him, "Yessuh."

Here's my next [picture]. It used to be Mister Lawyer Jester's. So he ask me to read him one mornin'. I told him first thing that I seen he's gonna be a lawyer and gonna be a railroad governor; that from a railroad governor he's gonna be a United States governor, the second year, he'll pass away. So he passed away.

I have lots of good white friends in Corsicana—looks like they'll stand by me—lots of colored ones. But lots of them look you in the face while behind yo' back they're diggin' a ditch fo' you. But I'm askin' the Lord to help me go on through.

Oh, they comin' [for advice about oil]. Yes, suh, I have them comin' all the time. Had one man here Monday. Oh, they come from different places, some from Oklahoma, some from down here at Teague, some from out here at Streetman. Farthest place that I've told about—I can't call the name of that place—oh, and I read them in California, too. That's right, had them come from California, everywhere. They come from all different places, directions, and everythin'. I can't call the names of the different people that come to me from far and near. There's so many folks come to see me— both white and colored. From everywhere.

I born in Mexia. I born in Mexia. I been here in Corsicana— soon will be forty years. Only lackin' but one year of bein' forty years. Next March be forty years.

All my life [giving advice]. I born that way. When the doctor came to Mama's house one mornin'—I born that way—Mama was in the house workin' with a white lady and she was in there. Says, "Aunt Marget, is you fixin' to born a baby this mornin'?" She say, "I don't know." She says, "Yes, you is, Aunt Marget"—Miss Annie Stroud at Groesbeck—she's dead now. She said, "Yes, Aunt Marget." She say, "I'm gonna phone to Mexia and get a doctor fo' you." So she phoned to Mexia to get a doctor and the doctor didn't come, so she phoned to Groesbeck and got a doctor. When the doctor got there I was done born.

The doctor come in and says, "I love fresh meat." Says, "You all done killed hogs?" Said, "Here's a nice hog heart, hog lights, and chitlin's." White lady say, "No, that's Aunt Marget's baby." "Aunt Marget's baby!" Says, "Well, I ain't never seen anythin' like that." Says, "I'm forty-nine years old"—not forty-nine, sixty-nine years old— "sixty-nine years old, and I ain't never seen nothin' like that. I waited on both colored and white an' I never seen nothin' like that in my life." Says, "Sho nuff!"

Says, "Miz Stroud, would you mind layin' a layer of paper on yo' dinin' room table and put a quilt on there and lay a paper on top that quilt?" She say, "I'll do anythin' fo' Aunt Marget." "Now put a sheet on that. Let me examine this thing an' see what it is." And so when he examined me my feet was back thataway and my arms down long. My head kinda knocked my shoulder.

He says, "Lookahere. She got a mouth full of teeth." Says [Aunt Marget], "What is a clairvayan, Doctor?" Says, "Some of them calls them fortunetellers." Says, "She goin' tell you things under the earth jus' like she can on top." Mama say, "I don't want that thing. I don't want that thing a-tall." So Miz Annie say, "Well, I'll raise her." Say, "I'll raise her." But Miz Eubank says, "Give her to me, Aunt Marget." Says, "Why don't you stay right around here and let her stay wid me?" And says, "You can—you can—you can have her." So mostly the white folks has raised me. And I'm so glad. I prayed with the religious white people, and at last converted my soul when I was ten years old.

Mama sent into the field one mornin'. She say, "Annie, you is ten years old dis mornin'. I want you to go on yonder in that field and chop cotton. Get that piece of hoe and chop cotton." So I started on to the field and picked up the hoe to go to the field. I heard a singin', "Amazin' Grace! How Sweet the Sound!" and the Spirit says, "Annie, go and pray," I dropped that hoe down. I said, "Lord, I can't pray. Lord, I can't pray," and went on down in the dust and walked right on back. Says, "Lord, I can't pray; Lord, I can't pray," and walked right on back up there. He said, "Annie, go back and pray." So I went back down and said, "Lord, have mercy! Lord, have mercy." Jumped right on up again. The Spirit called me right on back, "Annie, go back and pray." So I went on back down the third time and said, "Lord, have mercy! Lord, have mercy!" So I prayed from May seventh to September. Have mercy, Holy Ghost!

And so September, Mama was comin' in the kitchen one evenin' —she says, "I want y'all childern—we done picked all our best cotton —and I want y'all childern in the mornin' to get yo' sacks, and Annie, you git yo' flour sack"—you know I was small—"and I want y'all to go to the field in the mornin' up here in front of the house." I singin' to the children, I sing, "M-m-m"—I already happy—I singin' "M-m-h-m-m-h-m-m- M-m-m h-m-m u-u- m-m u-u uh-uu-hu- m-m m-m." I said, "We ain't goin' to pick no cotton in the mornin'." I says, "Icicles goin' to be hangin' thataway. Tree limbs all broke out in the yard." So next mornin', Mama got up to cook breakfast and send us to the field. She went to the back door. She says, "Oh, childern." Says, "Run here and lookahere." Says, "I ain't never seen nothin' like this befo'!" Says, "That chile tell that last night. Mama ain't goin' to whip her no mo'. I started to slap her but I wasn't goin' to slap her." Says, "Lookahere! Icicles high and hangin'—see 'em way out in the yard!" Said, "Come here, childern, and look!" Childern all run an' look. I was settin' way back in a little room like that room yonder—sittin' down on a little box, jest a'rockin', when Jesus spoke salvation to my soul.

"Annie, I want you to give up mother and father, brothers and sisters, friends and relations, and give up the world. Preach to the world of sin and salvation. 'Cause nobody livin' for nothin' but the Lord." I'm jus' so glad I don't know what to do. And I said, "Mama, I want to jine the church." "Annie, you ain't but ten years old"—said, "you ain't old enough to jine the church." Says Mama, "You ain't been to church a day in yo' life." Says, "The church is eight miles from here, no school or nothin', you have never been to church in yo' life." I says, "Mama, God converted my soul, you didn't." I says, "I wants to jine the church." So I asked the white peoples could I jine the church with them, and they says, "Annie, you can sing and pray with us—you can't jine but you can sing and pray with us." So I sung and prayed with those white people 'til I got a chance to go to church. I had to walk eight miles to church, called the Red Chapel, and stayed there 'til I moved into Corsicana. And I'm just so glad it was Jesus fixed me, it wasn't man. Thank you, Jesus. Thank you, my Father.

How do they know [about my work]? 'Cause of me sittin' down and tellin' 'em the truth. See, I tells so much truth in there—the future and the past—the future and past—all it is, the future and past. That's all people got in this world, jus' future and past. Yo' life —yo' palm—yo' blood circle into yo' blood. See, I reads by blood circlin'—yo' blood circlin'. It's not yo' lines or nothin', it's yo' blood that carries to the palms of yo' hand and through yo' skin. That's the way it goes. I'm differen' from whole lots of 'em. God borned me. Never went to school a day in my life. Not a day in my life. Where I was raised up it wasn't no colored folks' school, nothin' but white folks'.

I read cards, too. Yes, suh. The doctor tol' my mama, says, "Aunt Marget, you never whip Annie or scold Annie 'bout readin' fortunes. She'll look 'em in the face, jus' like she lookin' at 'em now, she'll look 'em in the face and at their palms and be through wid it. But if you go to beatin' and scoldin' Annie," says, "Annie'll read palms and cards." Say, "She'll get cards an' tell 'em." And he tol' the truth! I'm sure doin' that. That's right. Sho is doin' it. There's so many true things I tol' people and they tol' me about it. Yes, suh.

A man tol' me the other day. Come to me and said, "Annie," says, "I got five wells, jus' like you tol' me." Yes, suh. Says, "Annie, I got five wells. I didn't think I'd ever get to you but I've got to you."

Says, "I'm goin' to give you some money after while. Don't you be worried." I tol' him, "I don't worry 'bout nothin' like that."

That's the reason I said when they broke open my do' back there. I said, "Them's that got it have to lose it, and them that ain't got it, can't lose it."

I'm sixty-three years old. I sho is. All my life [in this work]. I jus' born that way. When I was eight months old, I walkin'. I was walkin' when I was eight months old. I always been a wise chile. My mama's seventh chile. Yes, I'm the seventh chile. That's what it says, a lucky number. Boun' to be. Boun' to be. Boun' to be. Sho nuff.

There's so many good works I did for the people—both white and colored. Can't none of 'em give me nothin' but a good name. I've always lived a life fo' Jesus.

A woman come here one day on the porch out there and her husband tol' me, says, "Miss Annie," says, "I been carryin' my wife to differen' places; no one has ever done her any good and I've heard of you." Says, "My wife haven't walked none in eight years." So I tol' him to go to the store and get some olive oil. While he was over at the store gettin' olive oil I was prayin' to her. She got up and went to walkin'—an' jus' shoutin' and I shoutin' too, to see her. Then, there's a white lady, about four months ago, came here—it's been a little bit longer than that—and I healed her. She come here and her husband say it's been about eight years since she walked. So she walked on out and got in the car. She was squeezin' me so and huggin' me so. And so I said I was goin' to stop healin' people but looks like I can't do it—the Lord put me here for it. I try my best to done quit but jus' can't do it. When God give you anythin' you jus' got to keep on.

God informed me of the truth. I can't help but tell the truth 'cause He says no lie you can't tell. And I'm so glad God fixed me.

—Annie Buchanan

LUCKY

STRIKES

3

American oil history moves forward with a succession of lucky strikes, from the Drake well on. Time and again luck forms the pattern of these wells: The well is drilled on a hunch, or on the advice of some kind of diviner; the backers are on the verge of going broke; the driller is ready to give up in disgust or despair. When it appears that luck has run out, when there is no apparent reason to go on, the well comes in, and the men who footed the bills are in the big money.

Or luck runs the other way. A well drilled for water comes in oil or gas or both. This happened frequently enough to be a part of oil folklore. The disappointment of the farmer who finds that the water for his cattle burns when a match is struck to it may be imaginary; it also may be real and as defeating as a dry hole.

No record was kept of the dry holes drilled on the same kind of advice, the same kind of chance. The number ran into thousands, and thousands of wildcatters went broke staking everything on a well in unproved territory.

The drama was not in dry holes but in gushers flowing wild, with oil spouting over derrick tops. These were the discoveries that people remembered and talked about, the discoveries that led so many to take the chance.

Corsicana Discovery Well

There is quite a coincidence in these first wells. The city fathers then, as in later years, sought a supply of water. And they let the contract to the drillers for a water well and were not pleased when they produced an oil well. There was quite a controversy as to whether they would pay for the drilling of the well because the contract was for water.

—*Martin Lowry*

My name is J. S. Simkins, my residence being in Corsicana, Texas, where I have continuously practiced law since my graduation from the University of Texas, and where I am still practicing law. I happen to have personal knowledge of the manner in which oil first became an attractive element in this state from the following conditions. My father, Judge E. J. Simkins of Corsicana, Texas, prior to the finding of oil in Texas, was in the State Senate of this state. And while there he carried two cherished purposes: one, to create a fine manual training school at the State Orphans' Home in Corsicana; and the other, to secure an appropriation from the legislature of sufficient moneys with which to drill a deep water well on the State Orphans' Home grounds, located a mile or so west of Corsicana. He succeeded in getting the appropriation bill through the legislature with which to drill this water well.

Mr. H. G. Johnson and Mr. Ritusbarger were awarded a contract by the state under which the drilling of this water well was begun and completed. My father and I practically every evening went out to the State Orphans' Home by buggy and horse to see how Mr. Johnson was getting along with the well, which was drilled with a cable. I do not have in mind at this time the exact depth that the well was to be drilled. But I think it was approximately four thousand feet. Mr. Johnson, with the aid of Mr. Davidson, stayed on the job continuously and at last succeeded in finding a tremendous flow of artesian water. I remember very distinctly when the word came in from home from Mr. Johnson saying, "Judge, come out, we have it."

We drove out there and found this great mass of water rushing out of this large-size pipe to a tremendous distance above the ground, and with water so hot that you could hardly bear to put your hand in it. And everybody was excited. At that time, the Corsicana Water Company was owned and controlled by Mr. Ralph Beaton, Mr. Fred Fleming, Mr. H. G. Damon, and Mr. Aaron Fergusson, I believe. Mr. Ralph Beaton was one of the most active men that Corsicana ever had in the matter of civic improvement. He was what you call a live wire. He went out to this well, came back to Corsicana, and apparently had a very lively talk with his associates. All these gentlemen of course went out to see this great water well, then began to talk about drilling a well in Corsicana. The well carried very fine minerals, as was shown by analysis of the waters. And they decided that if they could have the same character of well drilled in Corsicana, that they could promote a big plan there to make Corsicana a resort for the sick.

They thereupon decided to drill a water well south of the Cotton Belt railroad track, as it was then known. And they drilled this well to a depth of which I am not at this time informed, but got an enormous supply of hot artesian water like in the State Home well. And at the same time large quantities of oil came out of the well. I have frequently seen old men with long beards get down on their stomachs and drink this water with the oil on it, believing and stating that it would remove all kinds of ailments of the stomach. And these old gentlemen firmly believed it and accordingly drank the water with the oil on it.

Someone suggested that they drill further to the east and that perhaps they could find the oil. The result was they found oil all over east Corsicana, the oil rushing out going over the top of the derricks that were then I think about eighty-five feet in height as contrasted with the tremendously tall derricks of this day and time.

And it was a very frequent thing to see oil flowing down off of the roofs of people's homes, these wells being drilled in the back yard and up next to the house or anywhere they could find a location.

—J. S. Simkins

The Lucas Gusher

AL: I think it was probably in August we received a short letter from Mr. John Galey of Pittsburgh stating that they would have their man, A. F. Lucas, call on us in the near future with the idea of getting our price and see if we would move tools to a location near Beaumont, Texas, and drill a well for them, and that any trade we made with Mr. Lucas would be financed by Guffey and Galey. Now that was about all that this letter said. It was very short. So we didn't hear anything more from them till Mr. Lucas showed up.

Well, Mr. Lucas showed up on a Sunday there, and Jim was away someplace. So he called, and I took the old buckboard and the horse that we used to hustle around our tools and went down to the hotel and picked up Captain Lucas and took him around, showed him the oil field. So the next day, he and Jim got together. Jim was our business manager. They discussed the plan or the idea of moving a rotary down to Beaumont. So after much discussion, it was decided that one of us should go down and look the situation over. Well, a short time afterward, Jim went down and met Mr. Lucas there and went over the situation and agreed on a price of two dollars a foot for a twelve-hundred-foot test, Guffey and Galey to furnish all the pipe. We was to furnish everything else—derrick, and drilling equipment, and fuel, and so on.

So in October, early in October, we loaded our rotary on at Corsicana, and I went down and met with Captain Lucas. He met me at the train, rather. We went to the lumber yard, the Beaumont Lumber Company, and we bought the bill of lumber for the derrick. And then after that was attended to, we had to see about fuel. So they told us at the lumber company that we'd have to hunt up a young fellow name of Dane Price who had the rights—handled the slabs there for fuel over the town. So we drove around, and, of course, the Captain had lived there a good while, and he knew this young Dane Price. So we found him, and we made a trade for slabs to be used for fuel out on the well.

So that attended to, Captain told me that he had difficulties, that a carload of pipe was in there, but he couldn't get it unloaded. So I suggested we go out and see about it, and we did. We went out there in the afternoon, and I clumb up on the darn car and unloaded the carload of pipe which surprised the Captain very much. He couldn't think that—been led to believe that we'd have to have a hoist or something to do it. But we got it unloaded, and Cap, he was quite busy rolling it out of the way, you see, as I would roll it off of the car. What's been a mystery to me since how I ever got the joint of ten-inch out of the darn car. Got the eight-inch and the six-inch and the four-inch, of course, but I often wondered myself how I got that joint of ten-inch out. Pretty heavy. So that's how we got the pipe unloaded. He rolled it off, you see, as I rolled it down. Used four-inch pipe for skids, and I'd roll it up, you see. The standards came in on the car, you see, and I used those for skids that rolled it back, then rolled it up on the skids and out over the side of the car, and rolled down. And he'd roll it out of the way, keep it out of the way.

We went back to town, and I got me a room at the hotel and wired Jim to send the other boys down. They were all ready, of course, and I think possibly they caught the train either that night or the next night. They came in—that is, Curt and Peck Byrd. This fellow McLeod we had for driller, he was a few days later after we got everything moved out. So we went to work right away getting slabs out and everything ready and the slush pit dug and—necessary to go to work and get teams to move our boiler over.

The location was made in a way by Mr. Galey. The story is—Captain Lucas told me this himself—that when Galey came down there, he came in unexpected to Captain Lucas, and Captain Lucas was away. So Mrs. Lucas took him out to this place where these springs were, you might say. It was just a rough box in this little lake there that had been put in by somebody. We never knew who. There was about five of them there, that the rain water would collect there, and this gas would boil up through. The sulphur gas coming up through was stronger in some than in the other ones and would discolor them more. It was used for medicinal purposes. And Mrs. Lucas took Galey to this spot. So he decided there was where we wanted to drill the well, any place there. So when we moved in there, we just moved, set our derrick up where it was convenient, right close to those rough boxes, or what you might call springs.

It was rather a tough feat for us because we'd never built derricks. We tried to use this bill of lumber that a rig builder had given me, you see, dimensions and so on, to cut it to shape, but we didn't seem to have much luck at that. So we just strung the thing out on the ground and fit it to shape.

CURT: That was the first job, to build our derrick. The timber was wet, right out of the Neches River, and green, of course. And the timber wasn't sized then as it is today. One end of a two-by-ten would be an inch and a half thick at one end and two and a half inches thick at the other end, and it was really hard for us to handle.

Neither of us had ever built a derrick. Henry McLeod claimed to know something about building a derrick, but on arriving there, we found he didn't know any more than we did. So we planned this derrick. We made us a pattern. We knew how big the bottom of the derrick was, the base, and we knew how big the top of the derrick was supposed to be; so we made us a pattern and laid it right out on the ground, a pattern just like a woman patterned an apron. And we sawed—started from the base, laid our base down and put up our first girth. Then we sawed timber for the next section and so on until we reached the top. My recollection, the old Lucas derrick was eighty-four feet.

We started right away to moving our machinery in and setting up. We was possibly ten or twelve days building the derrick and getting ready to start drilling. Our boiler was F & T [Feren and Treft]. My recollection it was a twenty-five-horse boiler, F & T boiler. The engine was an Oilwell Supply, Wolf gear, and our pumps were—we had two eight-by-ten Smithvale pumps, and they were set up out of the bayou, pumping it dry. So we was forced to drill this water well.

AL: And that water well was about twenty feet deep. Got water. Put in a joint of pipe and, cussed thing, I got gas enough there that it would blow the water out of the pipe a little. But it wasn't enough to flow the water. We put a jet in, a steam jet, and jet the water out that we needed for boiler and for slush pit.

CURT: At this time, we started drilling our hole. We started with a twelve-inch bit, and we immediately, below the surface, went into a water sand. We fought this sand, losing our water and everything for several days. We finally set three joints of ten-inch casing. After this casing had been set, we went inside of the ten-inch pipe with a nine and a seven-eighth's bit, but immediately went into more water sand. This was very difficult for us, as we had never drilled in loose sand prior to this time.

We knew that several wells had been started on this particular hill or section that had only been able to get about four hundred feet deep, and the holes were practically lost where they couldn't go any deeper. So we was determined to make this hole twelve hundred feet, as that was our contract.

So we pulled bits one after another there and fought this sand until we decided that we'd just set our eight-inch pipe and then drive it into the sand as far as we could. This was done by keeping our drill pipe inside of the eight-inch casing with a full-sized bit at the bottom. We built a drive block out of eighteen-by-six timbers, and they were about eight feet long. We put a six-by-six in the back of these timbers, which made a "U" out of the timber, eight feet long, let's say. Then we put bolts through the other side so that the thing couldn't get off our pipe. We had our cathead line, a one-inch Manila line, tied to this block and over the derrick, and used it on our cathead for power. And we pulled that line, raised the block, threw the line loose and let it fall. Used it as a drive block.

AL: I got that idea from drilling cable tools on the cable tool work at Corsicana. We used drive pipe up there, and we'd drill as far as we could with our cable tools, until the hole would go to caving to prevent us going ahead, then we'd set in our string of drill pipe with a shoe on it. We'd drill through that, and in cases the pipe would follow right along. Other cases, we'd just have to rig up and just drive the heck out of it. And by fighting that up there so long with cable tools, why, it occurred to me that we could drive that eight-inch down there by washing the sand out from within, which we did.

And we got along fairly well, and I guess it proved quite a feat and quite a lot of work for we three because McLeod soon left about the time we got started at that. He didn't think we'd ever finish the well or get anyplace much. And he wasn't any too good a worker, anyway. Left Curt and Peck Byrd and myself. And we went on and finished the well.

We landed that eight-inch in gumbo there right around four hundred and forty-five feet, which is a pretty close measurement. We didn't keep an accurate measurement like we do this day and time, but we just measured by joints. We'd average up our joint as twenty feet, and they'd average about that way.

But we hit this gumbo at, oh, four hundred and forty-five feet. And then, after that, we got along all right until about six hundred and something when we had a little gas blowout. It blew the water out of the hole and did some damage to our rotary by cutting the grip rings off, the sharp sand coming out just like a blast furnace, and cut the collar on the drill pipe pretty badly, but no special damage, and soon subsided.

Well, after that happened, why, we were worried about maybe that might happen again, and the thing to do was, when we had the pipe in the hole, to keep it rotating. So to do that we agreed among ourselves. Peck and Curt both worked fine. By golly, they certainly deserve a lot of credit, and I've always given them credit for staying right there and pitching hay with me all the time. So we agreed then that to do that, we'd have to keep the pump running, and the rotary turning at night. To do that, we put ourselves on eighteen-hour tower. That is, every third tower, you see. So we'd come out and run the pump and keep the rotary turning and make what hole we could.

We got along that way all right, and on this special night, why, it happened to be my night to get up at midnight. We'd put up a length of drill pipe before the boys, other two boys, left that evening to go over to camp, which was about half a mile away, our little old shack that we slept and ate in. So I came on at midnight. Whichever one of the boys I relieved—whether it was Curt or Peck, I can't remember—but anyway, they hadn't made any hole hardly. It'd been pretty hard. Well, I thumped along there, you see, and along about three o'clock in the morning, the pump eased up, and the rotary began to turn with ease, and I commenced to let it down and go right along just as though there was nothing down there at all. Kept letting it down. Wasn't long till I had the whole joint down. Pump just run along as easy as could be. So along toward daylight I detected a gassy odor but didn't think anything about it especially, 'cause we'd had little soft streaks before, you see. But when daylight came, why, I could see on the slush pit here, the oil had come out in bubbles and bursts, quite a little bit of frothy oil on the dish and quite a little on the pit. So when the boys came out with my little bit of breakfast, why, we looked at it and sent Peck down to get Captain Lucas. He lived about a mile away.

So Peck walked down there, and Captain Lucas came up in a little while and wanted to know what it was, and I told him it was oil. So we discussed pro and con, and he suggested then we put up another joint and see how much of the sand there was. We did. Turned out to be about thirty-five feet of it. Well, we didn't know what to do with it 'cause we didn't have the hole in shape to—we drilled through it, you see. Didn't know, in those days, anything about a strainer [to strain] this soft sand off with.

Captain, he was pretty Scotch in a way. He wanted to save the string of six-inch we had laying there for another well. He must have had the fear if we'd use it there, well, maybe Guffey and Galey wouldn't drill him another well. Anyway, he decided the thing for us to do was to save that six-inch and hang our four-inch in there with a joint of six-inch on the bottom to the top of the sand, which we did, and waited then.

Course, Cap went to town and wired immediately for Mr. Galey. Well, it was three days before Mr. Galey could get there. When he got there, we had everything ready. We had our bailer and sandline, all equipment ready to bail it. Well, the very first time we ran our bailer, we ran it down to bottom. Pulled it out, why, the well made a little flow up aways, heaved it up almost to the double board, or the thribble board, about twenty feet up. Well, when we ran back in, we had quite a bit of sand in that bailer, of course. Went back in again, the cussed thing stopped three hundred feet up from bottom. This sand, soft sand, had heaved right up there. The pressure had brought it up and heaved it up on our four-inch.

Well, Mr. Galey had us run the bailer a few times, not very many times, and we could see that there wasn't any use in going ahead in that condition. So we rigged up, gathered up a string of two-inch. Went in and washed this well out to bottom. Washed a lot of sand and a lot of oil out. We tried to bail it again with the same results and tried the third time.

Well, it was getting up pretty close to Christmas. Mr. Galey could see that we couldn't make a success of it that way. As I said before, he nor none of us knew about a strainer to handle this situation. So he asked me, "Do you think you can pull that string of pipe?"

I told him, "I don't know, Mr. Galey."

"Well," he said, "I'll tell you what you do. You try to pull that pipe. Can't do anything with it the way it is. And set the six-inch through that and go on down and see if there's anything below." And says, "If you can get—*when* you get that done, well, shut down for Christmas."

Well, we had a pretty tough time pulling that pipe. Old Providence was with us. It would never happen again, I don't think. We managed to pull that string of four-inch out with that six-inch on the bottom, and set our six-inch and got our job done in time so that Curt and I caught the train for Corsicana Christmas Eve. We spent Christmas up there.

Curt and I left Corsicana on New Year's Eve for the works at Beaumont, landing down there January first and everything was ready, and we started to work, to go on down to finish our contract, which was twelve hundred feet. And we made very good headway for probably three days. Made a hundred and some feet, as I can recall now. And we got down to a thousand—about a thousand and twenty feet. Then we hit a crevice, seemingly a crevice, because if we'd turn the bit one way, it would go down five or six inches one way farther than would the other and turn a quarter turn, why, it'd stop and back up. And we fought that for a couple or two or three days, and I wired my brother Jim to send me a new bit. Our bits that we had used all down along the well were badly worn, just nubbins, you might say.

So I wired Jim for this bit, and he sent it down, and it arrived there on the morning of January tenth. I met the train, took it out to the well, and we put it on and was running this string of drill pipe back in, at about seven hundred feet or a little over in, when the drilling mud commenced to boil up through the rotary. And it got higher and higher and higher up through the top of the derrick and with such pressure, why, the drill pipe commenced to move up. It moved up and started to going out through the top of the derrick. Took the elevators, traveling block, and knocked the crown block off and fell over and didn't do much damage to the engine, but knocked the smokestack of our boiler down. The pipe went up through the derrick, then would break off in sections of three and four lengths at a time and fall over. Course, after that got out of the way, why, the rocks began to come out and gas to beat the cars.

It didn't last so awful long, but it died down very gradually. Well, we three boys then sneaked back down to the well after it quieted down and surveyed the situation, and I don't think I'm exaggerating to say that the mud was six inches deep on the derrick floor. And I had turned around to get a shovel to start to clean up, get some of that off the floor. And all of a sudden, a chunk of mud came out of the six-inch hole, full-size, with an explosion just like a cannon popping off. And that blew up with a little blue gas following it for a little bit, and then it quieted down, ceased altogether again.

Wasn't but a very little bit, I guess, less time than it'd take to tell it, probably, well, I walked over and looked down in the hole there. I heard—sort of heard something kind of bubbling just a little bit and looked down there, and here this frothy oil was starting up. It was just breathing like, you know, coming up and sinking back with the gas pressure. And it kept coming up and over the rotary table and each flow a little higher and a little higher and a little higher. Finally it came up with such momentum that it just shot up clear through the top of the derrick.

CURT: I was in the derrick at this time, and I couldn't tell you how I got down, but when I got down the driller had left the clutch in the draw works, and I got down in time to kick the clutch out. And by this time the pipe was going out the top of the derrick. And the other men had run and got out of the way, and, of course, I did the same thing. I ran as hard as I could and got away from the falling pipe, and no one was hurt from any of the blowout or the falling pipe.

AL: At first when we went down there to see all that mud and our drill pipe ruined—it was Mr. Galey's drill pipe, Guffey and Galey's, but it was our responsibility—we didn't know how much of the hole was ruined or what was in it. I rather expect that I was pretty disgusted. Of course, after the oil came in then and kept flowing and flowing we sent Peck on the run down to Mr. Lucas again. So when he got down to Lucas' house, why, Mrs. Lucas said, "Well, he's in town, but I'll try to get him." So she located him at Louis Myers' drygoods store there where he kind of made headquarters at when he was hanging around town. And he immediately jumped in his old buckboard with his old horse and beat it for Spindletop. And he came in due time and over the hill there, when we could see him, the horse in a dead run. Well, when he got so close, why, he just— well, there was a gate down there, I guess, but anyway, the old horse stopped, and Cap fell out and ran up. Of course, he was very heavy, you see, and by time he got up to me he was just about out of breath.

And he says, "Al! Al! What is it?"

And when I says, "Why, it's oil, Captain," well, he just grabbed me and says, "Thank God, thank God."

I daresay it wasn't over an hour, maybe, till people began to come. Some heard it, you see. You could hear this roar. And that afternoon they came in all kinds of conveyances. Lot of them walked.

Young fellows walked out there from town and come on horseback and wagons and buggies. Practically everybody came from town because from where we were for miles and miles there wasn't another dwelling. That afternoon, there was a big crowd there.

There was a fence. This big pasture, or what was going to be a rice farm, was all fenced, had been a big cattle pasture, you see. And they had a fence between the adjoining property but not over a hundred and fifty feet, I don't suppose, away. And people would come to that fence, and that was close enough because when the wind was in the direction, they couldn't come that close, you see, because the oil was traveling. That would go up there in this spray, and the wind would carry it for miles. Take the buildings in Beaumont; in a short time were all discolored. But a lot of that was from the fumes from the gas, the sulphur gas that tarnished the paints. And every house in Beaumont, I daresay, had to be repainted after that ten days' flow.

CURT: When Captain Lucas first got out to the well, after surveying everything, why, he wanted to go back to Beaumont and send Mr. Galey a wire. So he told us to keep everybody away from the well. So a little later there was one man who would pay no attention to our instructions and our advising him to stay away from the well. He crawled through the fence and started for the well. He'd gotten fifty yards through the fence when I caught up with him, and I walked on and talked with him and begged him to return, and he said, "No." He says, "You don't know who you're talking to." He says, "I was born and raised right here in this section, and I'm going to that oil well." And he went. By the time he got to the well, there was three or four other men crawled through the fence, and they also come to the well. By the time Captain Lucas got back, there was possibly fifty men around the well, got down as close as they could. And Captain Lucas blew up and said he was going to authorize the men to use a shotgun to keep the people out.

On Sunday morning there was possibly five or six hundred people gathered in this little pasture that was known as the Higgins tract of land. There was a gate on one end of this tract of land, and that was the only entrance to get in. That's where the people come in to see the well. They got as close as they were allowed to go. On this Sunday morning we'd had a heavy frost, and it was really cold, and Peck and myself had on slicker suits over our other clothes.

During the morning, it was reported that a Negro boy riding behind a white man on a pony dropped a lighted match. Everybody ran, got out of the closure just as quick as they could. They was afraid everything would blow up. And Peck and myself went to fighting this fire. We was about a hundred yards apart at the time the blaze started, and I was the closer. I got to the fire first, and I pulled off my slicker coat, and I went to fighting the fire with this slicker coat. Directly, Peck got there, and he pulled off his slicker coat, and we both fought the fire all we could. We burned our slicker coats up. We then pulled off our jumpers; we burned them up. And we pulled off our shirts, and we closed that off.

By this time, some of these men had begun to return. They saw it wasn't going to blow, and they began to gather. So there was possibly twenty men returned and helped us to fight the fire, but we put them to carrying boards from this barn. These boards was sixteen, maybe twenty feet long some of them. They'd carry them boards and throw them over the fence. And Peck and myself would get them boards and throw them on this fire. And the fire was narrow and burning at a distance and spreading at all times, but by throwing those boards down we would flop out sixteen to twenty feet of fire at one lick. But we had to leave those boards there a little while. If we didn't, the fire sprung up again. Sometimes we had to throw two boards down on the same place. It was that way. But in this way and with this amount of boards that we used, possibly fifty or seventy-five boards, the fire had burnt over something [more] than an acre of ground before we got it out. But we did put the fire out with those boards and the burning up of our clothes. No one was hurt other than we—our faces was blistered, hands were blistered.

AL: I think it was this Sunday morning about ten o'clock or something like that. I know I was coming up the hill on a horse. And I noticed this smoke burst up, you see, all of a sudden. Well, by the time I got there Curt had had the presence of mind—he was standing there talking, see, with these people—he had the presence of mind to jerk off his coat and commence fighting this fire. Somebody on a horse there had dropped a match, and it'd gotten started. But then other fellows jerked their saddle blankets from under their saddles and helped him fight it out.

When I got there, Curt was out of breath. I remember just as well as though it was this morning. He was all smoked up, and this smoke had gotten all over him, and his clothes were all dirty, and coat was ruined, and he was out of breath. He'd fought it, you see, through the help that he got there. Of course, a lot of them ran, you see. Some of these came back and helped him out. And they beat it out with saddle blankets and coats. That was the only real close call we had, but if it'd ever gotten to the well, I don't know what we'd have done with it.

CURT: When Captain Lucas come in there, he was very much elated over what had happened, but didn't know what he was going to do with the wild well. There was no tankage in the country. The oil was going out just like a river in the lowlands that they intended to put in rice, and there was no way of stopping the well at that particular time.

AL: Wires came in there from, I think, as far away as San Francisco offering to shut it in. I think the highest offer, probably, somebody sent a wire in, they'd close it in for ten thousand dollars. Of course, he wired for Mr. Galey right away as quickly as he got composure enough to go back into town and send him a telegram. Well, it was three days. Mr. Galey was down in West Virginia, and they couldn't catch him in Pittsburgh right away, but they got him down in western West Virginia. Well, he caught a train and got in there the third night. We'd arranged for a room for Mr. Galey up in the Crosby House. And I met him at the train. Jim had never met him. Jim didn't know him. So I met him at the train, took him over to the hotel, introduced him to Jim, and Captain Lucas showed up.

So we went up in this room, and we was talking about the well and so on. And it wasn't a little while when J. S. Cullinan came up. So J. S. sat in on and listened to the propositions and so on, and Mr. Galey finally turned to Jim and says, "Well, you boys drilled the well. What do you think about shutting it in?"

Jim said, "Well, Mr. Galey, I think we can do it."

He said, "All right, go to it."

So Jim got busy the next day. It was his idea. Give credit to Jim for all the ingenuity about getting things together and collecting them to shut it in while we other boys went out there to clear things up, get the rotary and the rotary equipment away, get it from over this well, and straighten up the pipe the best we could so we could work, and do our watch job too, of course.

So he arranged for the timbers and the clamps and one thing and another, and I went over to the railroad—better not tell the Southern Pacific this—but I swiped two railroad irons. Of course, they were light little railroad irons out there on the switch track. And we drug those over with the team that hauled our slabs, you see. We fastened those up on the derrick, the girths of the derrick. And to those, why, we bolted a carriage arrangement and had a kind of a crate affair fixed and assembled—all these fittings, the valves and the "T" and the connections, you see, and all in this crate affair, and it was all bolted solid to this here carriage that was on the railroad irons. Of course, those railroad irons were secured at both ends very securely to the derrick.

Well, then we got off. We had it all arranged and thought we was ready. Why, the well was still throwing out rock every once in a while. Throw it up high as you could see. They'd go up, you see, and come back down. I've got some of the oil sand—the only, I think, that's left—up in the sunroom there now. So he said, "Well, now, we'd better not shut that in today for one of those rocks might damage our valve, might knock it off." So we waited till the tenth day, and it seemed to clear itself altogether and hadn't made any rock that morning at all. So he came out about eleven o'clock, eleven-thirty, "Well, boys, how's it been acting?" And we told him hadn't made anything. Says, "Well, let's shut her in."

During our drilling operation, we'd gone running the drill pipe in and out of the hole so much to change bits, you see, we had riveted, in a way, riveted that protector on that pipe. Impossible to screw it off. So as I was the unmarried one, why, I took the responsibility to go in there, and it took me a whole afternoon to sit astraddle that pipe and cut that off. Got diamond points and a hack saw and one thing and another and just worked in there very patiently. J. S. Cullinan told Jim, said, "Now, Jim, you watch that kid." Says, "He's in great danger." Says, "If he hits a spark there, why, he just—it would be impossible for him to get out."

So the boys stood right close all the time I was doing this. Well, I cut that in two and got it sprung apart enough where we could get it off, and I had a half-round file and three-corner file, you see, and the hack saw. I dressed those threads up all around, got them in perfect shape—and this oil was raining down on us all the time, you see, just a constant rain of oil.

But before I started this operation, I went into town and got me a pair of goggles and got adhesive tape and taped all around those goggles and my eyes. I had a hat on, of course, a slicker hat, you see.

We had slickers. I had a slicker suit on, slicker hat. And that would drain the oil off.

It took me the whole afternoon to get that down so it was in shape to screw on the "T" or the collar. Then we worked up with the "T" and valve and sledge nipple and so on. I suggested to Curt, I says, "Curt, you turn the valve there, will you?" And he rushed in— of course, we had slicker suits on and a slicker hat, you see, to protect us from this oil. So Curt rushed in and closed the valve. Just like that, it was over.

CURT: It was a successful job. No one was hurt; only I was the one to close the gate valve, and I was overcome with gas, which was the first person to be gassed in the Gulf Coast.

AL: Then we covered the whole thing up with a mound of earth, you see, so that if fire did get in, it couldn't get to the [well]. There was oil all around there yet. Our old slush pond was covered with oil, and what grass was left was all saturated, and the ground was oil-soaked. So if it'd ever get a fire, it would just burn for hours, you see. So we covered that up with a great big mound of dirt.

CURT: The oil all went into the flatlands in that section, and during this time, while the well was flowing, it was also some heavy rains, and the oil was washed away with water, a great deal of it. The railroad had shipped several carloads of sand or clay into a culvert, a bridge, that was on the downside of the country, with hopes of holding the oil. And that place filled up. That whole section of the country filled up and held the oil till this big rain come. And then finally run over the railroad track up to Gladys City and was caught fire by a locomotive at that point.

This was possibly twenty to thirty days after the completion of the Lucas well, because I had moved my drilling rig which had drilled the Lucas well over onto Gladys No. 1 and was drilling on that. And I disremember just how deep I was when the fire came. But it was an awful bad fire, while it wasn't a destructive fire because it was burning up waste oil that we had no place to put. And that finished the lake of oil, which was the worst fire that I've ever seen up till now.

It burned mighty fast. It caught fire along in the middle of the day, we'll say, from this locomotive, and it burned until about four o'clock in the evening and had got clear across that end of the lake. It was possibly three quarters of a mile up to the other end of the lake. So they thought best to get rid of the oil; so they set a fire at the other end of the lake so it would burn up quicker. And when these two fires met, it created a great explosion. When the fire would meet, it would throw hundreds of barrels of oil up in the air, and it'd explode up in the air and plumb down to the ground. And just jarred the whole country just terrible. Well, that would throw that oil back maybe a hundred yards, and it'd rush right back up and pick up a few hundred barrels more in the air and explode again.

So it just played back and forth there for three or four hours thataway. And people all over that country was scared to death. And during that time, there was a shower of rain, and the smoke had gone over Beaumont and as far as Orange. In all directions of the country it was just so dense a smoke that you couldn't see anywhere. So the rain coming through this black smoke ruined the paint on most of the houses in Beaumont, possibly all of them, and some damage was done at Orange, I was told. But it wasn't a destructive fire for the reason it was burning up waste oil.

—Al and Curt Hamill

Goose Creek Discovery

It came in at night. I seldom went out on the field. But Judge Reed was associated with Mr. Welch and the others, and they had been expecting to bring the well in for several days. A good deal of gas was showing. And I don't remember what time in the night it was. I think it was about eleven or twelve or one o'clock, away in the night. Somebody rushed up on the front porch and banged the door loudly. I thought somebody had been killed or hurt, and so Mr. Gaillard got up and went to the door, and Judge Reed was bringing the news. He said, "The gusher has come in, and the whole country's running away with oil. Come out and see it. Come out and see it." And he was so excited he was fairly jumping up and down. My sister was staying the night with me; so she went out when she heard him banging on the door so loudly. She thought somebody had been killed or something dreadful had happened; so she went out there. Judge Reed grabbed Mr. Gaillard around the shoulders and waltzed him around the porch, and my sister went out to see what was happening, and he started to grab her, and she drew back, and then he got so he could explain what had happened.

—Mary Gaillard

The Duke Well

I stayed with them [the Gulf Oil Corporation] until the fall of 1917, when I, along with Bill Wrather, who was the geologist, decided to quit and go out for myself. We had no particular plans and certainly did not have any money, but we'd saved up a little, probably three or four hundred dollars each, and we thought we could trade in leases and at least make as good living as we were making and probably accumulate something. So we resigned and decided to go together.

He was the geologist in north Texas for the Gulf Oil Company, the old Guffey. Bill had come down from Pennsylvania. He was a graduate of Chicago University and held a master's degree at that time. Later he had a doctor's degree conferred on him after he had made quite a reputation for himself as a worldwide and recognized geologist.

Bill and I, the first thing we did, we went over to Walters, where I'd seen all the work that was done by Munn and his crowd, and we leased several tracts over there. One was the Patterson land, two eighty-acre tracts of land, and we paid two dollars an acre for it. In about a week we sold those two tracts for eight dollars [an acre] apiece to the Humble Oil Company and thought we had made a whale of a big deal.

Not long after that, if I remember it was along in September, the word reached Wichita Falls that a well had come in down at Ranger. That was the old McCleskey well drilled by a man named Gordon. We got in an old Model-T car and drove all night to get to Ranger. Went out to the well, and things had gotten pretty wild around there. The well was blowing, and it was a beautiful oil well.

But by the time we got back to town that afternoon, why the town was full of men, and people and farmers were trading in acreage. Well, they were way beyond our means right off; so we couldn't do any business. We stayed there another day, then decided to come on back and see if we could raise up any money to make any deals with.

We did not have very much luck; so after studying our maps awhile, Wrather said, "I know, let's get away off down there and get us a bunch of wildcat acreage somewhere where we can make a trade," and said, "We might as well go down there and look for it."

Said, "There's no use in trying to fool around Ranger." I said, "O.K."

So we started out and wound up down at Stephenville, Texas. From there we drove around over the country and down to Comanche in Comanche County, and Bill thought there was some prospects up on a creek known as the Banner Creek. We came back to Wichita Falls to see if we couldn't raise some money, and while here we talked to Mr. R. O. Harvey and Mr. Frank Kell. They told us that if we could find some leases down there that we thought were worth the money, that they'd be willing to pay for the leases and take care of us for an interest in them, and that all we had to do was to draw on them with the money. So we went back and wound up at De Leon. We talked to several men there, one being a banker by the name of Lowe in the First National Bank. Another was a lawyer named Hanson. They told us that there'd been no leasing in that country and no interest in oil other than a barber who had been fooling around trying to interest everybody to join him in drilling a well up near Hog Creek, which everyone knows is Desdemona, but in that country the little town was known as Hog Creek, because it was located on the bank of a little creek known as Hog Creek.

We drove out to Hog Creek to make the acquaintance of the barber, who was Shorty Carruth, and he was a real character. The first man, however, that we talked to was Dr. Snodgrass, the local country doctor. Snodgrass said that there'd been a shallow well drilled on his little farm right north of town by some men from Strawn three or four years before, that Shorty Carruth had been instrumental in gettin' 'em to come down and drill this well. They went to a total depth of somewhere around seven hundred feet. We asked him how he knew he had some oil, and he said, "Well, they bailed some oil out, and it was on the ground." We went over and met the barber and talked to him. Of course, everybody in town thought Shorty was crazy, and so it did not excite anybody when we went in to talk to him. He said that he had a well that was two hundred feet deep right west of town, and that Tom Dees and another man from Midlothian had furnished him the money to get that lease.

We asked him to go with us out to look at it, and he did. He had a small Star machine with a little twenty-horse boiler out there. He was out of money and had no pipe or anything else to put in the hole, and so immediately he wanted us to furnish some money to drill this well deeper. He then told us about the well that was on the Snodgrass place and how much oil it had in it, and practically the same story that Dr. Snodgrass had told us. Well, we didn't believe him, or at least we were skeptical. Oh, after talking to him a while, why we found out that he and Tom Dees and this other gentleman had approximately three thousand acres leased, but it was all north and northwest of the little town. We asked him what he thought about us getting some acreage in there. "Oh," he said, "you can get all the acreage you want if you'll drill a well." We went back to De Leon that night, had a talk with the banker and Judge Hampton about what we had learned, and they said that they'd heard that story but they didn't place much confidence in it, that everybody thought Carruth was crazy.

The next morning Bill got up and said, "Tell you what let's do. Let's find out about that well." I said, "All right, how're you gonna do it?" He said, "We're gonna run a sample on it." I said, "All right, let's get another string to put down that hole." So we went to the drugstore and got a bottle—oh, just a small bottle, you know. Probably ten ounces or something with a big mouth, like quinine used to come in, and we bought us a couple of balls of twine. They claimed there were three hundred feet in each ball. So we drove back out to Dr. Snodgrass' and got the old gentleman. We went up to this well. We ran a bottle in there on the string, and the casing was still in it, and fortunately there was nothing that we ran into. However, between four and five hundred feet down we hit fluid of some kind; and when we pulled it out, sure enough we had some oil in that bottle, a little oil, a little water. So we proved that the old gentleman was telling the truth.

Well, of course, that excited us, and we didn't say anything more to Carruth. We just told the doctor not to say anything about it, and that we were going to see if we couldn't get him a real well drilled in there. The doctor was a very fine old gentleman, a well-educated old man, and he assured us that he'd help us every way he could. We asked him to investigate us and see whether we were reliable and whether what we told him would be the truth, and he said he would. We went back to town and asked Mr. Lowe to do the same thing, and he said that he would.

Then the question came up was how to proceed on getting this acreage together without any money and what to do; so we had a strategy meeting and decided that we'd have to find out a little more about where we wanted the acreage. Bill said, "We've got to determine if there's a structure ring here and find out where the thing lies." I said, "Yeah, but how're we gonna do it? We don't have a plane table. We don't have anything." He said, "Well, come on. Let's see what we can find out."

We went out there the next day, began to talk to the natives about the thing, and one native said there was a limestone that showed up over there in the creek somewhere, and it was kind of a blue lime, and that that same limestone you'd find in all of your water wells around there. Most all of the wells were at least four or five feet in diameter. There were no bored wells. They were all dug. I said, "Bill, why can't we follow that limestone and see where it goes?" He said, "Why, sure, let's do that," and said, "And you know what I'm thinking about, that we can measure the depth of it if we can determine what our altitude is at the different locations, and if we can find out which way this thing is in here, if it's in here at all."

Well, we took our string and got us some pieces of iron for a weight to put on the end and began to measure the depth of this limestone; and sure enough, that limestone tipped to the south and east, and it was about the same height all the way out on to the east. Then it tipped off again on the north side. Well, that was up where Shorty Carruth had his acreage. That didn't bother us much, but we hadn't determined where the high point on it was, so the next day we started down Hog Creek. We walked along down there, and there was a little stream of water in it, and finally the water disappeared on just a sand bed, and a little further down, why, right out of the bed of that, was a huge rock of limestone, and it was exposed there for a distance of, probably, oh, one eighth of a mile. Then the sand covered it up again, and we walked on further down. The water showed up. Bill said, "There's the highest part in this thing. That limestone's gone up like this, and that sand's blown off of it. Here is the highest part on that structure; so," he said, "let's get out our map and plot this stuff out from right here and get it together if we can."

Well, we were very much excited then; so we went on back to town, got our map and marked out what we wanted of the area; and then the question came: How to get it together without exciting those natives? I reasoned this way: If we tried to lease it one farm at a time, why the first thing you know Shorty Carruth and those other fellows would be right in the middle of the thing.

But sure enough, in a couple of days, why Mr. Dees showed up. Carruth had written Dees a letter, and Tom Dees came up there, and he said, "I want to go in with you on this thing"; and we told him no, we didn't want any partner. "Well," he said, "where are you going to lease?" And we told him we didn't know. "Well," he said, "I want to get in here and take some leases right along with you." We said, "Now we can't put this deal over if you do that. We'll do this with you, Dees. If you'll let us alone and let us get our property together, we won't disturb your property up there. It looks like you've got the best end of it, and you keep on and get you some more acreage on that side and let us alone down where we are."

"Well," he said, "I want to take some around the edges where you're going." But at any rate he finally agreed that he'd kinda lay off, and so I went to work to get all those people to agree on a deal without signing any of them up. I got most of them to agree, and we had a meeting at the schoolhouse one night, and I told them I wanted to treat them all alike, that even though some of them had more land than the other one that they would all get benefit out of a well, and that I'd give them a dollar a farm, and we'd put it in the bank and we'd start a well within six months. Well, some of them didn't seem to be so warmhearted, but old man Koontz and Mr. Merrick, they all said they wanted to help, and old Dr. Snodgrass; so that night I had a notary public with me, and that night before we'd left there we'd signed up three thousand acres of leases—about ten or twelve farms. Maybe more, but I got those in the bank.

That was the first time I'd ever heard of that deal, but that was the only way I could figure that I could get it all over. Well, it wasn't three days until the news had gathered that we were drumming up acreage for a well. Of course, the lease hounds were in there, and they were all trying to buy leases. However, I kept on until I got six thousand acres. Then I reported back to Wichita Falls that we had this acreage, and we sat down and worked out this kind of deal that Mr. Harvey and Mr. Kell and Mr. Perkins would underwrite the cost of a well, and Wrather and I would have a quarter interest in the deal, carried free in the first well; and we would try and make a deal on some of the acreage if we could and relieve them of the drilling obligation, and if that was the case then we would have to revamp our deal so they'd have an interest in it the same as we would.

They agreed to that; so Wrather got on the train and went to

Pittsburgh to see his old friend F. B. Parriott, who was with Benedum-Trees. He got up there, and John Kirkland was there and Jim Lantz and Mike Benedum—to talk it over with them; and old man Kirkland said he'd come down here and look the thing over, and he did. In the meantime, why, we had made a deal with a drilling contractor to move a string of tools in there.

I came to Wichita Falls with Wrather, and I met with Mr. Kirkland and Harvey and Kell and Mr. Perkins, and they decided that was a good deal, and we would split the quarter interest among us. Then we got the leases in shape, which took quite a good deal of time on account of the fact that none of 'em had an abstract. We had to go to the records and run the records on every tract of land out there.

We asked the Pittsburgh crowd if they would accept the titles. They said they would accept the titles on whatever Judge Hampton said, and if they turned out to be good then they'd send some lawyers down to do whatever they wanted done about the titles, but they were to take them. We said, "Well, we're not going to warrant them, but if you don't want to clear them up now, why it'll be your baby to clear them up later." They said, "All right, we'll take our chances." The group up there that went in on that trade was Mike Benedum, F. B. Parriott, Charlie Parriott, Jim Lantz, John Kirkland and a couple of gentlemen that I didn't know. They were all practical oil men that were reared right there in the fields of Pennsylvania and had been interested with Mike Benedum in many of his ventures.

I spent Labor Day at Wichita Falls, which I think was around September the second, and started back down there that Saturday evening about dark or right after dark, and about two o'clock in the morning I'd gotten as far as Albany and started out of Albany going south. As I was driving down the road outside of Albany, I saw a flash in the sky a way to the south, and then the flash died down a little bit; why, it flared up again, and I saw it begin to go up and down, and I knew there was a well on fire somewhere down there. Well, I knew it was right in the direction of either Ranger or Desdemona, but it looked like it was too far away for Ranger, but it didn't excite me much. I thought, "Well, there'll be somebody there having a big fire for the next day or two." As I drove into Putnam about three-thirty that morning, why old man Caldwell ran out of his house. They had a little telephone in his house. He ran out of the house in his underwear and flagged me down. He was so excited. He said, "That new well over at Desdemona, at Hog Town, is on fire, and they've been trying to get you." I said, "No." He said, "Yeah." So I said, "Well, I saw it when it caught." So I went on up to the hotel and woke up one of the drillers that was staying there that was on the Cathey well.

By using that steam and putting the nipple over—that swedge nipple—we dropped it over the top and turned the gas out to one side and shot the steam on the well and put it out and kept the water going on it then for twenty-four hours to cool it off to where we could get in there and do something with it. The well, after we got it hooked up, the well made about twelve or thirteen hundred barrels. I don't know how much it was making to start, but probably made a good deal more than that when it started on fire at first. It was all flowing, and a lot of oil was going down the creek that had escaped, and it was burning there for a mile and a half. So that is the way the Duke well came in, which was the discovery well at Desdemona.

—*Landon Haynes Cullum*

The McCleskey Well

I very distinctly remember that first well coming in [in Ranger, 1917], on the John McCleskey place just adjoining ours, to the south of us. The well came in—oh, along I guess in the middle of the afternoon or early afternoon. That particular moment I was alone up in the peanut field [on my father's farm] shaking peanuts.

That well blew in, and it blew over the derrick—I don't know how far over the derrick, but more than twice as high as the derrick it looked to me like—a very deep green color, and then it turned a gold when it broke at the top, into an open rosebud formation before it fell to the earth. The gas pressure caused it to make a great deal of noise. And it scared me. I was just a youngster, thirteen years of age at that time. I thought that the world was going to turn inside out or something, probably in the process already.

I immediately left that peanut field and have never, never returned to shake the rest of the peanuts. I ran out of the patch and down Eastland hill, the west side of Ranger, and down the main street and announced to our neighbors and friends that something had certainly gone wrong out at the oil well that they were drilling on the McCleskey land.

I guess I'm the one that carried the news [of the discovery]. I've read in books and papers that others broke the news, but I doubt that any of them got to town [about three miles from the field] any quicker than I did.

I told them that something had happened at the McCleskey well, that the inside of the earth was in a liquid form and it was coming out. I didn't know—it might be oil, but I could tell them for sure that there's something wrong out there, that it's entirely different from anything I'd ever seen before, and I didn't know, I just had never seen an oil well, but I had seen the thing at a distance and something green and then gold, going way high over the derrick and making a very loud noise. It scared me, and I left the peanut field to report it.

Well, it seemed to get around immediately then. Everyone in town—and I don't think that's an exaggeration when I say everyone in town—got on their horses, in the buggies, or some of them had cars; others just walked over the hill in a southwesterly direction to see what the score was, to see what had actually taken place. And I know that I went on out with my daddy and mother, we went over there. And, of course, I stood at a safe distance; I was still afraid of it. There was something about it that scared me, that I couldn't get over for a long time. I thought that was one of the largest crowds of people that I'd ever seen, and it was an exceptionally large crowd for Ranger.

However, that was just a forerunner. Starting the next day, the people did start swarming in there, and as the days rolled by the people in larger numbers came into Ranger. I can distinctly remember the trains, Texas and Pacific Railway, from the East or from the West, freight train or passenger train. Passengers were not merely riding just inside those trains. Some were even on the cow catcher, others were up on top of the box cars, others were on top of the passenger coaches of the passenger trains, hanging on the sides. I've actually seen men hanging on with their hands to the open windows on the passenger coaches. That's how crowded these trains were coming in here. Others were coming on wagons or trucks and so on. They were just coming in from every direction and they kept coming for quite a while.

At that time, of course, I didn't know who any of them were, but I later found out and got acquainted with a large number of them. Surprising, all types of people, from all walks of life, and from all parts of the country and from foreign countries, came into Ranger. I can't quote figures on it from memory, but I've been told that approximately thirty-five thousand came in there within one month's time.

And I don't doubt it, because I distinctly remember there was no place for lots of them to sleep, no decent place for any of them to eat. I distinctly remember one individual who came there penniless; in fact, I loaned him one dollar out of my pocket, which to me in those days was a large sum of money. He told me that he was broke and he was hungry, and I never knew what it was to be hungry, but I didn't want to see anyone else go hungry, so I loaned him the one dollar. Six months later that man was a millionaire. I don't know how he bought the first one, but he bought leases and royalties and sold them.

—*John F. Rust*

Killam's First

And then we organized the Mirando Oil Company. And came back in January 1920, and took charge of the operations. I didn't know anything, but nobody else knew enough to know that I didn't know anything. So we started out on our development program, but we had to wait nearly a year before we could get enough water in the tanks down where we wanted to drill. And so I remember that we bought the first complete drilling rig for thirteen thousand dollars. 'Course it wasn't very big, it was a forty-five-horsepower boiler and everything in comparison. That was a rotary rig. You can't buy a modern pump for that now, you know. And I remember that our drill stem was four-inch line pipe and pretty weak stuff too.

The first well we drilled had a little showing in it but not enough to make a well. And we moved about a quarter of a mile east which ordinarily would have been the wrong direction to move, moving down dip, you see. I should have been moving probably up dip.

And we moved on the second location and when we got down to around 1461, we had what we thought was an oil sand. We shot a string of casing in it without cement; we didn't know anything about cementing in those days. And we started to cap this well.

Well, we had about sixty foot of rat-hole below the sand—why we had it I don't know. Ordinarily that, at that time, would have destroyed a well if there had been one there. But anyway when we started to bail it, that casing dropped down in the rat-hole about sixty feet, cut off our sand. And ruined our well.

"Well," I said, "skid over here about sixty feet and let's see what; let's drill another one." So we moved over and started the third well. And we got down 1413 feet and we were just about out of fuel. The driller said, "If you'll let me set the casing here, we can do it with what fuel we got. But if you're going to go any deeper, you'd better get some more fuel down here." Well, it didn't make any difference to me. I didn't know any better. So I told him to go ahead and set it. So we set the casing at 1413 and then bailed it to see if the second-hand string of casing had any leaks in it. And when we bailed it we had an oil well. If we'd had more fuel we'd gone on through that and we'd never found that oil field, you see. So it looked like Providence was really helping me out.

—O. W. Killam

East Texas Discovery

[The Miller farm dates back more than a hundred years. Originally it was several thousand acres, and in fact it was the large part of Rusk County and it was sold off in pieces until about 1930, when there were just a thousand acres left. The farm was originally acquired by General Andrew H. Miller and passed from him to his son, who was John C. Miller, and from John C. Miller to Dr. Henry L. Miller, who was the father of H. C. Miller, K. C. Miller, and Daisy Miller, who was later Daisy M. Bradford.]

The Joiner lease was originally acquired on the Miller farm in 1925, and when the five-year lease had lapsed, no production had been brought in. At that time before H. C. Miller would lease the block back to Mr. [C. M.] Joiner, he made a provision in the lease that he procure his own driller before he'd let Joiner have the block again. So at that time Mr. Miller went out in Louisiana and got Mr. E. C. Laster. At that time there were John Joiner [C. M. Joiner's son], E. C. Laster, Walter D. Tucker, who was formerly a banker at Overton, Texas, and numerous others. John Joiner did more real active work than anybody connected with it, I think. Laster was quite a capable driller. He brought the well in after having, oh, half a dozen drillers before him, I imagine.

We didn't have any kind of trouble at the well. The driller always phoned me to phone Dad Joiner. They phoned and told me that they had [lost] the hole of the second well, and they didn't know what to do. So I phoned old Dad Joiner, and he said to tell the boys to get Mrs. Daisy Bradford's tractor and tell them to skid it any way that she wanted to do out there and tell them where to move the well. She and I sat on the hill to watch them move the rig. It was an old rotten rig, worn out. When they started they asked her which way to move the well. She said, "Move it the way of the least resistance, boys. Just move it downhill." When they started downhill and got about two hundred fifty feet, Mrs. Daisy jumped up and said, "Stop, boys. Drill right there." The derrick began to wobble a little, and she said, "Drill the well right there." They stopped and that's where the discovery well came in.

—Mrs. H. C. Miller

BOOM

TOWNS

4

The Lucas Gusher blew in, and Beaumont had a boom such as had never been seen before, though there were foreshadowings in the gold-mining and silver-mining towns of the preceding half century. The pattern set by the gold rushes was repeated in the oil booms: In both cases a new resource was discovered; there was an immediate influx of population too rapid and too great to allow the normal process of community growth.

But the pattern was somewhat modified in the oil fields. For one thing, the value of the product was much greater. Boyce House has reported that "the entire output of gold in California in 1849 was only $10,000,000, while a circle with Ranger as its center and having a radius of forty miles takes in an area that in 1919 produced $90,000,000 worth of oil and well in excess of $90,000,000 the year following." The Ranger production was only a small fraction of the total.

Also, it was easier to get to the source of wealth. The basic system of trunk railroads had been completed well before 1900, and while one might have great difficulty in getting the few miles from the nearest railroad town to the oil field, it did not take long to go from San Francisco to Beaumont in 1901, or from Pittsburgh to Ranger in 1918.

The migrations to oil fields were large and rapid. Twelve months after the discovery at Sutter's Mill in 1848, some 42,000 people from the United States had made their way to California. In two years following the discovery of oil at Spindletop, the population of Beaumont jumped from nine thousand to fifty thousand, twice the population of San Francisco in 1850. Sour Lake, hardly a village when oil was discovered there in 1903, had in a few months a population of ten thousand. On Batson's Prairie there were some twelve or fifteen houses scattered over an area of eight square miles when oil was discovered on October 31, 1903. By January of 1904 the population was estimated at ten thousand. Ranger's population climbed from six hundred to thirty thousand in a year. Borger, founded in February 1926, had a population estimated at twenty thousand the following December. Western Oil Corporation's No. 1 Desenburg came in at Mexia on August 2, 1921. The population of Mexia rose from four thousand to forty thousand "in a few days."

In the California gold rush, and in the Klondike, the people who rushed in were grown men and women, temporarily or permanently released from family ties. Boomers in the oil fields in great numbers took their families with them. At Spindletop, Sour Lake, and Batson, women and children lived as close to the derricks as possible, to share dangers with the men, to live their days and nights in the mud and sweat and sound of the oil fields. The absence of all-weather roads made it necessary for workmen, even after Ford had placed automobiles within their reach, to live near their work. And for this reason each oil town had its ragtown—groups of shacks and tents for the workers, eating places, and often saloons and houses of prostitution.

What more than anything else determined the character of the boom town was a legal principle known as rule of capture. With rare exceptions an oil pool would extend under the land of more than one owner, and with equally rare exceptions more than one operator or company would hold leases in the field. Under common law the owner of the land is owner of the minerals under it. This law had raised no problems as long as the minerals were solids, which would stay in place. But oil and gas migrate from areas of high pressure to areas of low pressure. When a well is drilled into an oil-bearing formation, a low pressure is created at the bottom of the well, and the gas pressure brings oil from the surrounding area, often extending beyond the boundaries of the surface owner's property. The legal question was, who owns the oil recovered. There seemed to be no precedent in Anglo-American legal tradition. But the Supreme Court of Pennsylvania in 1889 found one in the common law governing the capture of wild game. Wild deer, for example, have no fixed habitation, but wander over various estates. They belong to any man who can capture them on his own premises. Oil and gas, the court held, being of a feral nature, should be governed by the same rule, and should belong to the man who captured it on his own land. This decision established a precedent that was followed throughout the United States until modified by a series of enactments and sustaining court decisions beginning in the late 1920s.

It meant that if an owner or a leaseholder drilled an oil well, his neighbor had to drill too, to prevent the oil from being drained from under his land. The courts held that a lease contract contained an implied obligation on the part of the lessee to protect the interests of the lessor. Thus if one company held leases on the farms of A and B, and had completed a producing well on A's farm, it must, even though all the oil could be recovered by the single well, drill immediately on B's land; otherwise A would get the oil that had been in place under B's land. Then each would produce oil as rapidly as possible in order to get his share. If they had agreed to restrict production, they would have been subject to prosecution under the anti-trust laws for an agreement in restraint of trade.

The economic effects of the rule of capture are almost incalculable. The discovery of a major field (except in time of war) would depress the local price of crude oil below the cost of production. Thousands of wells were drilled that were technically unnecessary. Trillions of cubic feet of gas that might have been used for fuel or energy or to supply basic chemicals were wasted, and the underground pressure that would have brought the oil through the porous reservoir sands to the wells was dissipated, leaving as much as eighty per cent of the oil in the ground.

The social effects were equally undesirable. There would be from two to three years of feverish activity and then the field would be "drilled out." A few pumpers, gaugers, and other maintenance men would remain, but most of the new population would leave. Neither public agencies nor private capitalists would or could make the investment necessary to provide what we now call a decent standard of living for the temporary population. Railroad traffic would be clogged, and such local roads as then existed would be turned into quagmires, so that transporting essential supplies became in some places a major problem. Workers generally lived in tents or shacks, or crowded flophouses that rented cots in eight-hour shifts, the "hot bed" system. Sewer and water systems could not be created where they did not exist, and where they did exist, they could not be extended to meet the needs of the expanded population. Health laws could not be enforced in the eating places. Epidemics broke out from time to time.

The boom over, a community had gained in wealth and permanent population and attained the stability of a typical American town. Its people would resent its being judged by the two or three abnormal years of the boom.

But the repetitions of history are never exact. Many fields escaped the social disorder that we have, with reason, associated with the boom town. Much depended upon the temper and size of the stable, preboom population. Presumably, with the approval of their constituents, the officers of Hardin County had not enforced the liquor laws before the discovery of oil, and it was hardly to be expected that they would enforce them during the booms at Sour Lake, Batson, and Saratoga. But whether they could have enforced them if they had wanted to is doubtful. The cattlemen and farmers that constituted the bulk of the preboom population were completely swamped by the newcomers. It might be stated as a law that, other factors being equal, social disorder in a boom town is directly proportional to the ratio of the new population to the old. Thus Beaumont fared better than Batson and Borger.

Another important factor was the ownership of land. If Best fared better than Breckenridge, for example, it was partly because at Best there was one principal landowner, the University of Texas, which could refuse to lease land for purposes it did not approve.

Men who were active in Texas oil during the first forty years of this century are not in complete agreement as to when and where the last big boom took place. Some say Borger, some say Kilgore. But they are all agreed that the boom days are over. The modification of the rule of capture has made proration possible and permitted the orderly development of fields. Improved equipment has reduced the number of man-hours required to drill a given footage of well or to lay a given mileage of pipe line. It also calls for a different type of workman. Indeed, one does not have to be overly sanguine to say that partly because of public education the American workman has attained a status that discourages the exhibitionism that used to manifest itself in drinking and fighting and wenching. Equally important has been the construction of roads, which have made the shack town unnecessary. Now if a wildcat well is to be drilled, the first work done is the building of a road from the nearest highway. This is a matter of economics. With the road-building machinery now available, it is cheaper to build the road than to haul the equipment through mud and sand.

Spindletop

Well, of course, all kinds and classes of people come into Beaumont on this Beaumont boom, and there were no houses in town for the people. I don't recall just how the houses went up in the town of Beaumont, but out in the oil field in the beginning it was tents. There was worlds of tents went up, and then lumber was cheap at that time, and they built little shacks scattered round over the country there for two or three miles. Go out in the woods and find where someone had throwed up a little shack out there; and in less than a year's time the country was full of those little houses. Later, why, they begin to build better houses up in the town of Beaumont.

There was different kinds of stores come in there. The first outfit that come in there was a couple of Jew boys. They put up a very small shack and sold handkerchiefs and socks and suspenders. And finally added work clothes, just in a small way. In fact, there was three of those boys to start with and one of those boys, something went wrong with him, and the other two give him a whipping. They started him out of the field there and whipped him with a wet rope. I didn't see it, but it happened. I heard it. From where I was I couldn't see it. But there was an awful yell went up with different crews of men. That boy run, and they was both of them after him, and every time they could get to him, they'd hit him with that rope. And he fell down three or four times, and so we never did hear of that boy afterwards. There was just two in that firm after that day.

There was lots of fights there, yes, fist fights. There wasn't no serious fights. In the beginning I don't remember of anybody killing anyone there. But they'd fall out over different things and have fist fights. And after the pipe liners come in there, 'course the saloons come in there. They sold beer and liquors of all kinds there. Beer was a dollar a bottle. And so on. And there was lots of it drank. And those pipe liners, why, was more of an Irish people, I'd guess you might say, and they were a fighting people. And they would get tight and scrap amongst themselves, you know, and get up and shake hands and go on.

—*Curt G. Hamill*

We moved to Panhandle in '91, in a covered wagon, clean across the plains up there. My dad was going to get rich raising wheat. We stayed up there four years and came back to this country. We lived in Hondo, Texas, and I went to school there. Then we moved back to Uvalde County, north end of it. Then we moved to Del Rio in '99 in a covered wagon. Then we moved from Del Rio to Seguin. I stayed there just a year. My folks stayed there and I come to Beaumont on a freight train. Got out of a boxcar right by Fuller's Restaurant on Pearl Street, right by Pearl Street, at four o'clock in the morning.

I'd never been in a restaurant, you know, to order anything. I was nineteen years old. I went in a French restaurant up there and I saw some sardines setting up there. I said, "Give me a box of them sardines." I only had a quarter in my pocket. That's all I had left. And he set them out and I give him a quarter to give me the change and he said, "They are two bits a box." I said, "Good God Almighty." And I walked from there to Spindletop, five miles or six, about six. And the Park Street was dust about six inches deep and they'd spread that oil on it to keep the dust down. And then I was sick. I got out there at noon and went to work at one o'clock without any dinner. Just had them sardines for breakfast, you see. And I went to work for the Drummers Oil Company on a rig. And I stayed there for two years. 1901. And the mud was everywhere, good God Almighty, everywhere. 'Course they had wagons and mules and horses, I mean wagons to haul the stuff from town out there for the rigs.

—Frank Redman

Those who were at Beaumont in the early days will recall the trouble of finding a place to rest. My first three nights in Beaumont left an indelible impression upon my mind. I paid three dollars per night to sleep in the loft of Broussard's livery barn. The bed consisted of a limited amount of straw, covered with a tarpaulin. It was a democratic bunch of men that roosted in Broussard's stable. Millionaires and working men tried to get a few hours of sleep. I'm certain I never heard a more wonderful exhibition of snoring. The voices covered the entire range from basso profundo to coloratura soprano. There wasn't any designated footage that a man could use up in the loft of Broussard's barn, and as I recall it, the fellow next to me, who did not take off his shoes, kicked me a time or two in the stomach, and sleeping next to him was not very pleasant. I changed bedfellows the following night.

In visiting the joints, I met a young fellow by the name of James, and he suggested that I talk with his mother about a roosting place. I made a deal with Mrs. James. I could sleep in her back hall at two dollars per night, if I would furnish cot and so forth, fold it, and store the cot and other personal chattels on the back porch each morning. No extra charge was made or credit granted for the horde of pestiferous and voracious mosquitoes. I had to go to a neighborhood barber shop each morning to wash my face, but to eliminate this slight inconvenience, I invested in towels and washed under the outside city water tap.

The city water of Beaumont back in those days was soupy. Its odor clearly indicated the presence of alligators, bullfrogs, and fish. Everyone soon learned if the water was used for drinking purposes that it caused severe stomach cramps, or what was locally known as Beaumonts. Toilet facilities being limited, a bad case of Beaumonts called for biddings as high as fifty cents for the immediate use of a toilet. We didn't have pay toilets in those days. Most of them were outside. Later, I bought water for drinking purposes. My recollection is that water was brought into Beaumont by barge, from some point up the Neches River.

—H. P. Nichols

One of the boys, he come around where I was working and he says, "Will, I see your saloons here, they've got a whiskey in it, that you can take that whiskey and put it on two brickbats and they would jump up and go to fighting each other, right there," he said. That's about the way Spindletop was. It was just a saloon here—and around over it.

—William Joseph Philp

I lived out at the edge of the field here, right—oh, I guess closest well was a couple of thousand feet of our house. It's more of a shack part. All the whole place was—wasn't any houses to amount—was worth anything. It was mostly what we know as oil-field shacks. Out at the little town here at Spindletop—some of them called it Spindletop, but it was gradually known by Gladys City—was the post office there. Some of them called it Guffey. Some called it Spindletop. But

Gladys City was the permanent post office out here at that time. Men with their families living right up close to the derricks, about as close as they could get sometimes. They didn't have anyplace else to build a place. They were just shacks. Just box-frame wooden buildings. Just a common old one-by-twelve box with cracks batted up with one-by-fours.

They cooked on the old-style wooden stove. For their wood they got what we gathered up around from the old derricks at that time.

I brought them [my family] here in 1903. Yeah, I bought a little place somebody had; it had been built for years before or something, and I had a chance to buy it. It had calmed down in 1903. It calmed down a whole lot. Most all of the wells had quit flowing then and gone. We began drilling with these shallow stands then.

—*Claude Deer*

Dr. R. L. Cox—the old gentleman died a couple of years ago —started his career there. And he had three little horses. And old Dr. Cox was a very, very, very nice man, good man. A lot of my desire to become a physician was through Dr. Cox, because he had a little office on the side of this drugstore. It would accommodate a bed and an old gasoline stove and a little cabinet that would take about ten or twelve little rows of surgery equipment and stuff like that. This and three horses and one saddle consisted his practice materials. And when he didn't have any business why he would run out and get on his horse and ride down to the end of the street a mile and a half at sixty miles an hour and come back. And old Lee [Cox] and the little old horse would both be blowing to beat hell, and run in just like he'd had big business.

And in a little while why somebody would come in with a leg broken or an arm broken or a leg to cut off or something of that kind. And we'd all gather over there to go into this little doctor's office. And I learned after a time that the way not to be pushed out was to get in and get behind the door. And also learned that the way to accommodate him was to reach down and get the old washpans that he had there, or dishpans or whatever they were, and set them on the gasoline stove, which had two burners on it, and start heating water. And when he'd push everybody else out why he'd leave me there. And he'd say, "Get kit number four, number seven, number six and put it in the water."

Well, that was big business for me and I still had an opportunity to stay in and see what was the matter with the man that he was going to cut a foot off of, or cut his hand off, or cut his finger off. I've cut a many a finger off. I've cut a leg off many a time, just sawed it off with the saw. I went in the old butcher's shop and got it. I've done a lot of things of that kind when Dr. Cox was in need of help. He had no nurses, and the druggist wasn't there a lot of times; he was busy in the store. And maybe I was the only individual in the little office with him. And many times he said, "Get hold, kid." And of course he was working with the little vessels to keep blood from spurting here and there.

Maybe he was trying to use his own saw, and his saw wouldn't work. He said, "Go across there to the butcher shop and get that saw." And I knew which one he wanted and I'd come running back over there with that thing and he'd say, "Saw it off." Maybe he'd have the man's leg up between his leg holding him like this and lay it up against the bedstead like that and finish the job off. And he'd go ahead and trim it up. Well, sometimes with an anesthetic, most of the time not. They didn't have time to administer it. Most of those men were men that were, you know, hard workers and worked down. And he could just give 'em a shot and go ahead and operate.

I'd say the fatalities were very small in comparison to the losses that you have now with all the modern doings. In other words, near as I can explain it, in the early days we didn't have any more fatalities over accidents and things like that as we do now.

—*H. C. Sloop*

Negroes at Spindletop

Time of the year was in February. It was cold and it was wet for about four or five days before it warmed up any. And what I mean, it was raining. And I worked, just the same, with the slicker pants and the slicker jacket.

I had this shack. And then Mr. W. P. Markley came and bunked with me. South Africa. We called it South Africa. It was named that because there was so many niggers that worked in earthen tanks and so forth like that, that they called it South Africa.

We never had no trouble, though, with them. They never did bother us. They worked just like ordinary men, only they did lots of singing and going-on among themselves. But they never did bother nobody. I never could see why that they wanted to run them off because they were handy and they did lots of real honest-to-God hard work. But they decided that they didn't need them there and so they run them off.

The work was done by the Negroes. The shoveling, the scraping and what you call it, what do they call those long scrapers? Fresno, the old fresno. And the short scrapers. They used practically all of those and mules.

They decided that it would be better off to have the niggers away from the field. They felt like at that time that they were taking up jobs that some white man probably would be glad to have. And they decided that it would be best to have them removed. So there wasn't so much disturbance about it. Now I felt this way; the best thing I could do is to stay out of it all. I stayed clear away from it. Shooting went on but there was very little damage done. And they didn't do no harm, now that's true, that's true. And I thought that was a wonderful thing.

—*Frank Dunn*

Now one time there was a bunch of colored folks went out there to work and I had a brother in that gang. He says, "Now, they won't allow no nigger to do oil work. They can drive a truck and go through there with a little lumber and anything like that, you can have nigger drivers. But you can't get out and take the brake and drill for oil. We just won't stand for it." They rounded up a bunch of niggers working out there and scared them pretty bad and that's about all the trouble they ever had. They never come back no more.

—*William Joseph Philp*

Sour Lake

But we was very fortunate. Most of it was fist fighting. None of my bunch didn't get killed. There was a number of others dead. And they even had gambling devices out on the sidewalks, shell games of all kinds, besides what they had in the saloon. The deputy, I believe, at that time, was a fellow by the name of Buck Summers. All they done was to hold inquests and pick up dead bodies, try to regulate the traffic so people could get through with boiler wagons.

But we didn't think it was any tougher then than we think it is now. You get into a crowd like that; you get accustomed to it, and if a man got killed you'd look at him and forget it until the next day, because probably you'd see two more bodies the next day, you see. And it wasn't anything to get excited about.

I never heard of a man getting highjacked in Sour Lake in early boom days, and I've saw as much as ten thousand dollars on each crap table, a man standing with his back to the window, where they could have reached in and got it. They didn't have to highjack it, because they was taking it fast enough with those crooked dice and crooked cards; so, they didn't have to highjack. And you take a number of boys that come right in with the payday, walk up to the bar and spend a whole ninety dollars and never take a bath nor change clothes.

Drinks was on an average of fifteen cents for whiskey and fifteen cents for beer, two for a quarter, and everything was very normal. Wages were three dollars for twelve hours, but a boy could dress up pretty nice, could get a haircut, and a shave, and take a bath for three dollars. You can't do that now, because a pair of khaki pants will cost you more than that. Haircuts was twenty-five cents, shaves fifteen cents, pants fifty cents, and your shirt fifty cents, you see. And twenty-five cents for a bath; your board and room was a dollar. So we still had a little money left out of our three dollars.

There was women of every type, all types, from the smallest to the largest, and from the tenderest to the toughest, and we had lots of fighting among the women; of course, I don't remember of any women getting killed. They generally got beat up, somebody would separate them. I believe Nella Dale and Grace Ashley put on the best bout I ever seen. I think they fought an hour and fifteen minutes before they were separated. And when they quit fighting they didn't have on enough clothes to wipe out a twenty-two.

This fight taken place here in Sour Lake, and that woman was the best fighter I ever saw. I never did know what her real name was. We called her "Mooch." And she was from Cripple Creek, Colorado, and she was kind of every man's pet hero because she could always come out under her own power when she was drinking, and she was a good fist fighter.

Women and men. You could, if you wanted to see a fist fight, if there wasn't one on in the block you was on, walk over to the next block, you'd see it; it would be there, waiting for you. And the bunch I worked with—I hate to say it—but they was double-tough.

I believe one of those saloons in Batson with a palmetto roof on it, and then in Humble we had one that was made out of slabs from the sawmills. But that saloon got so bad they made a sawdust pile out of it. If they couldn't get your money, they'd get you drunk— and one that didn't fall to the sawdust, they'd take it [money] off of you in the back rooms. So then we got tired of that. There was a railroad running beside of it where they hauled logs. And one night we got a bailing line and put it around it and put a clamp on it, and when the log train come by, we hooked it onto the log train and scattered that slab saloon about four hundred yards right down the railroad track. That's the way we tore that one up, because it was trimming the roughnecks.

Then in Batson when I went over there they had a constable— his name was Bunk McAdams—and when they sent the Rangers in, Bunk didn't like it, you know; he was constable and he thought he ought to be able to handle the situation. And Bunk did handle it pretty good. He stayed about as drunk as they did, and they all got along pretty good and spoke each other's language. So one night Bunk got drunk, and he come out and started some rough stuff and talked about the Rangers, what all he could do. Well, Tom Franks was the least man in the Ranger service. Well, Bunk he weighed over one hundred and forty pounds. Well, when he got to the top of his glory, and there was a big bunch around, Captain McDonald looked over and says, "Go over and unharness him." So he went over and taken his guns off, and then Captain McDonald turned around to the crowd he says, "Men, the state of Texas sent us in here to fight," and says, "we like our job." Well, they didn't have any more trouble with the Rangers, because they knew that old man meant business. And things was pretty quiet as long as those Rangers stayed in there and there was very little killing there, and we had lots of fist fighting. That was common.

—W. H. (Bill) Bryant

Batson

I lived in the Caledonia Boarding House. I wasn't here at that time [the beginning of the boom], but I would say there wasn't over, oh, twelve houses on a prairie containing several thousand men.

The Caledonia Boarding House was a two-story house. It was run by a Scotsman by the name of Simpson. There was some ten or twelve rooms for sleeping, and the rooms were about twelve feet long and about eight feet wide and the furniture consisted of two cots, and if you had a suitcase and other things, you had to put it under the bed. Then, if it was a bad rainy night or daytime, you would lay there in bed and dodge the raindrops from the leaks. There was mud in the front of the boardinghouse and all around, and when they went to sweep the floor, they taken a hoe and raked the mud out of the dining room.

Twenty-six dollars a month. That was the regular rate. For room and board. I was drawing ninety dollars a month. And I might say the buying power of a dollar then was much greater than now. They served good, substantial food for working men, but I cannot say as to how well cooked and how clean it was. It was not.

And the sanitary conditions was terrible. No sewers, nothing. And I have seen in the ditches and along the pathways and wherever low places would be water, and that water would lay there until a green scum would come over it. I have often wondered why we all didn't die of the cholera. And no screens, and flies by the billions. No protection at all.

There was a man by the name of Mr. Scarpins. Was a very good man and an enterprising fellow, and he tried to better the condition. And he went around among the different people and got up a collection, and he got up the money, and he got a couple of broom-tail ponies and a sled, and he went to work to build a road and drainage, and that was the first that ever was done.

That was about the year 1908. And I recall very well there was a rig builder by the name of Rumbaugh, and his children, his boys, played out in front of the house. And was a big mud puddle and water, and they played in there. And he made the remark, he says, "I thought when I was giving to Mr. Scarpins a little donation to build up the road, I was helping the health conditions of the community. My boys has always played in the mudhole all day, and for some time they never seemed none the worse of the effects from it, but after we got the place drained up and cleaned up, my boys was sick."

I would say, including the saloons and beer joints, which Texas at that time granted a right for a man to sell beer but not whiskey, and I would estimate, considering the whole territory covered, there would be at least thirty saloons. There was the Sazarac Bar and Tom Matson and the Jordan Brothers, American Bar, Crosby House, and, oh, Bird and Mars.

The Crosby House was considered the fanciest at that time. The Crosby House was a large, two-story building. The main part of it was a saloon and bar. To the rear of it was a gambling house and a dance hall. And the upstairs was rooms, and it was occupied by questionable characters.

And then another saloon there was Tom Thompson. And another by the name of Doc Harris. Doc Harris run a saloon. And this Doc Harris I've made mention of was a medical doctor, but did not practice. But he run a very elaborate saloon for that time, and he had a dance hall and a gambling room and a whorehouse all combined. And just to the rear of his place was a very large two-story building, and that was run as a Negro whorehouse. And often white men was there.

Doc Harris was what you would term, I would say, a typical saloonkeeper and gambler. Very neat in his dress, and, as usual at that time, a very loud, flashy vest and a double watch chain. And always had his shooting irons at easy access where he could soon take hold of it and get into action. But with all that, he was a very tenderhearted man. He was very sympathetic. I recall in his place of business that there was a man killed, and he was brought in there, and his bartender formerly had been an undertaker. And he laid the body out and prepared it for burial. And Mr. Harris come in and said—and this little boy about ten years of age was standing there —and Mr. Harris said, "Now, gentlemen," he says, "you're welcome to leave the body here, but," he says, "I believe if I was you, I would take him someplace else. My reason for this is, now here is this ten-year-old boy standing here by his father, who is a corpse, and what could his—would his—impression be when he grows to be a man to think that his father was laid out in a saloon and a gambling place?" And we then carried him across the street to the El Main Hotel lobby, which was a respectable place run by the—a lady, and she gave us permission, and we put him in there. I don't know of any funeral services held here, but the body was taken to Corsicana and, I suppose, had burial services there.

—James Donohoe

We really averaged when we were slaughtering—oh, we averaged from one to eight beefs a day, and that many hogs. We had a branch of the French market out of Beaumont out here, and they usually averaged from five to six, and that many hogs every day. I got them right out there in the prairie and in the thicket, razorback hogs, and just knocked him down and clean him and take it in there and weight it down, and get your money and walk off.

Well, the country people out here—they had a nice thing of it. You take a lot of wild game in this country, and they sold squirrels, two for a quarter, and a man could buy a box of these old-time black-powdered shells for forty-five cents—I believe—but then, you hardly ever missed a squirrel with one of them, you know.

They had a fellow they called French Joe. He would buy most any kind of a fowl, and when it didn't look enough like a duck to be related, he would tell them that it was a prairie chicken. It would be a crow or some of these marsh cranes we called them or something like pelicans—something like that. He said it was a prairie chicken.

—W. E. Cotton

Boom-town Undertaker

Well, I started hanging around the livery stable when I was a pretty small kid, but to handling dead people or corpses, my first experience was at Batson in 1904. And Mr. Jones was manager for Crater and Rangam that owned the stable. And I slept at the stable at night; and, consequently, it was my duty to unharness and take care of horses that come in late and answer the telephone and go out in event of a death or an accident and haul the wounded or crippled or dead ones to the livery stable, which was known as an undertaking parlor in those days. Of course, they didn't call them that, but that's what they was used for. And we had a hearse, which was a solid hectagon-shaped vehicle.

'Course, the only undertaker—licensed embalmer—that we had in this country was over at Beaumont. And when the occasion arose for us to have an embalmer, why, we had to send to Beaumont and get one. But on several occasions I taken it upon myself, by the authority of the undertaker, to start embalming procedures before he arrived. And on a number of occasions I completed the job before he got over here. And, of course, I knew enough about it to take care of a person that was all together, but I didn't know enough about it at that time to take care of one that was mutilated or tore up in an accident or cut up in a fight. I eventually learned it, but I never took an examination as an embalmer for the simple reason I couldn't pronounce those words, much less spell them. I've embalmed lots of people in my lifetime, but I'm not a licensed embalmer.

About the most exciting run that I ever had was one night in the wintertime. It was dark and had been raining, but it had practically quit. There was a roughneck killed in the field. I've forgot now how he was killed. I believe he fell out of a derrick. And I went in the field and loaded the body. Started back to the livery stable and got about halfway back, why, I met a bunch of men with lanterns milling around in the road. And they stopped me and asked me what I had, and I told them I had a body. Says, "Well, throw him out. We got some more work for you to do." Well, they drug him out to the side of the road and left him there. And pointed to a tent over there that had a light in it and a bunch of lanterns around it. And says, "Go over there." So I went over there, and there was a dead woman and a baby. I loaded them both up and went on to the livery stable and unloaded them and put them on what was known as the "cooling board" in those days, and put in a call for my bossman.

About the time I got that done, why, a couple of roughnecks come in and says, "When you get time," says, "you can go back down there in the bushes about one hundred yards from where you were and," says, "you'll find two more."

And I says, "All right."

So I went on back down the road and picked up the man I'd laid beside the road at first, and brought him up and put him in the wagon bed back in the livery stable. Didn't have no more boards.

In the meantime, old man Cyrus Jones, the manager, had come on the job, and I told him there was two more down there where this woman and baby came from. And in the meantime I'd learned why there were two more down there. This lady's baby had taken sick, and she'd got up to give it a dose of medicine or tend to it, and some rattlebrain drunks shot at the light, see, through the tent. Killed her and the child both. And these roughnecks and rig runners around there, they caught those two guys and hung them to a sweetgum tree. And them was the two men that I went back and got. I cut them down and hauled them in.

Of course, we had any number of accidents. They wasn't accidents, either. There was quite a few killed in street fights and saloon fights, and most of that was just a guy get too much whiskey and figure that he was cock of the walk. And there was always somebody a little further down the road to give you what you're looking for, so we had shooting scrapes quite often. That usually wound up with dead men because our medical aid and efficiency didn't amount to much then.

Of course, if a guy got cut in two, they might put his guts back in there and sew him up. That's about all. If he lived, he lived; and if he died, he was just dead.

Of course, we used to make our own coffins. That is, they came from the factory knocked down, you know: four sides and four ends and four tops and four bottoms and four sets of hardware in a little box. The stable boy, he nailed them together. I've nailed many a one of them together.

Most of them are in unmarked graves. And of course some of them got a Christian burial, and some of them was buried by the roughnecks. And on one or two occasions me and a Negro was the only one in the cemetery or where we buried them. And me and a white boy—I was about sixteen years old and he was about fifteen —we buried one beside the road by ourselves, a dark corner on the way to a cemetery. And it got dark on us, and we decided we'd went far enough; so we pulled out the side of the road and buried him beside the road. We found a stump hole that was partially dug. So we just buried him deep enough we figured the hogs wouldn't root him up. I think they had a record of who he was, off of the payroll. Otherwise, they didn't know any of his people or where he was from. They just knew who he was.

There's any number of them, you know, were floaters—lot of them traveling under assumed name. Some pretty tough characters going and coming. We had bank robbers and gamblers and cutthroats of all kinds and descriptions. The name they gave was all we knew; and whether it was right, that was just a supposition. But there's a lot of them buried in unmarked graves.

I pronounced a benediction over several of them. I done the best I could. Quote a little Scripture rather than just drive off just like you was leaving a dog.

—Plummer M. Barfield

1. Corsicana, 1898. First Texas oil field.—*Magnolia Petroleum Company*

Trost

2. The Lucas Gusher, Spindletop, Texas, January 10, 1901, marked a significant point in American oil exploration. —"Oral History of Texas Oil Pioneers," *Texas University Library*

3. Al Hamill, driller of the Lucas Gusher, as he appeared at the dedication of the Spindletop Monument fifty years later. —"Oral History of Texas Oil Pioneers," *Texas University Library*

4. Days were hectic and nights were more so in Beaumont, Texas, in 1901 when 50,000 people descended on this town of 9000, drawn there by the magic of "black gold." Ham and eggs were a dollar a plate, a cot was $5.00 a night, and even a pool table commanded a good price for a night's lodging. Trains were important, too, because hundreds came in on the morning train every day and left on the evening train, that being one way to "stay" in Beaumont.

—"Oral History of Texas Oil Pioneers," *Texas University Library*

5. Gushing the Higgins No. 4 for the benefit of sightseers and speculators at Spindletop, 1901. Notice brass band at right. Credit must be given to Trost, who had a photography shop in Port Arthur, for recording much of the early oil history in Texas.
—"The Oral History of Texas Oil Pioneers," *Texas University Library*

6. Reportedly the first saloon at Spindletop, about 1901. The hanging decorations are hornets' nests.
—"Oral History of Texas Oil Pioneers," *Texas University Library*

7. From lowly beginnings. The Texas Company moved to this building from the Temperance Building in Beaumont in the early days of the Spindletop boom.
—*Public Relations Department, Texaco*

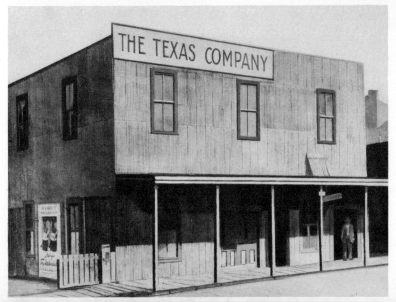

Fire Shoe String District
Sour Lake Tex 1903

8. Sightseers on their way to a fire on the Shoestring District, Sour Lake, Texas, 1903. Wells were drilled in long narrow lines, hence the name "shoestring."
—"The Oral History of Texas Oil Pioneers," *Texas University Library*

9. Rio Bravo Oil Corporation fire in the early days at Spindletop.
—"The Oral History of Texas Oil Pioneers," *Texas University Library*

10. In early oil fields, derricks often stood close enough for men to walk from the floor of one to the floor of the next. This scene was repeated in many of the early boom fields.—*Standard Oil Company of New Jersey*

11. When the boom came to Batson in 1903, there was no jail. Until one could be built, prisoners were chained to trees on Fannin Street to sleep off a drunk or to await transportation to the county seat. The man in this picture may have been a bona fide prisoner, or he may have been a local resident obligingly posing for the photographer, more likely the latter.
—"The Oral History of Texas Oil Pioneers," *Texas University Library*

12. At Sour Lake, where oil was discovered in 1903, roughnecks used materials supplied by nature. These huts framed with poles and thatched with palmetto leaves furnished some protection from rain but none from mosquitoes.
—"The Oral History of Texas Oil Pioneers," *Texas University Library*

The Flu Epidemic at Newtown

You have inquired about the boom and the living conditions and the condition of educational institutions and other facilities at Burkburnett and Wichita Falls during the real peak of the 1919 to 1921 boom, following the completion of the Fowler well.

Of course, there was a tremendous influx of people. Crop conditions had been very poor over most southern Oklahoma and western Texas, and there were thousands of families who were suffering for lack of enough food and clothing and shelter to carry them through the winter months. A substantial number of these people from both southern Oklahoma and West Texas got the best means of transportation they could, usually a team and a wagon, the old covered-wagon type, with a few household possessions, and possibly with a tarpaulin tied to the side of the wagon to make a kind of tent or shelter. And some of them brought a few chickens or a poor milk cow, and they came along the roadside leading west from Burkburnett for three or four miles. And when winter came on, why, a good many of them had found employment in the new oil field. There were many and many hundreds of them who were still unemployed and underfed and definitely in need of sufficient housing. And we had what you and I now know to be the worst flu epidemic we've ever had in the United States.

I was serving as field director for the Red Cross at the time in charge of Red Cross field operations at Call Field near Wichita Falls. I contacted the commanding officer, and Major Atkinson, who is today practicing medicine in Wichita Falls, was then in charge of the medical corps. And we agreed that the presence of the violent type of flu at Burkburnett only fourteen miles from Wichita Falls, was a definite health hazard to the trainees, the young fliers in training out at Call Field, and we got the government to assign some doctors and nurses to try and relieve the situation.

Cold rain and a little sleet came about the time we got the crew from Washington, and we asked the people of Wichita Falls to contribute in order that we might find shelter and food and warm clothing and medicine for the people, many of whom were suffering from flu and exposed in these covered wagons and under these tarpaulins. I remember it quite well because I took a young lieutenant, a doctor, and a hardboiled gal, a former Regular Army nurse, an Irish gal, out in my car and we started west.

The mud was terrifically heavy but the Marmon was a terrifically good pulling car. And we'd pull up and go in and investigate. In one place, you'd find a mother dead, with a little six- or eight-month-old baby crawling around over her breast, trying to open her dress. And you gather her up, and look around, and her husband is sick over there, and a little boy.

We had wagons and a lot of volunteer workers. We had lumber and mattresses, beds, bedding, sheets, of course, and towels, and nightgowns and pajamas, and medicine and food, but it would take four or five men an hour or two to fix that particular family up. In the meantime, the lieutenant and my Irish nurse and myself would move on. I think on our first trip west of Burkburnett, we gathered up some six or eight dead men, women, and children, and they continued to die until we found temporary shelter for them.

The people in Wichita Falls were most generous and helpful. They shipped lumber and bedding and food and clothing by carloads. As I recall it, the railroad hauled it to Burkburnett free of any freight charge, and the teamsters, the oil-field haulers, hauled it out to where it was needed without any charge. And the workers from Wichita Falls and Burkburnett were working without charge. And it was possibly one of the saddest sights I've ever had to experience, and since I was director of the Red Cross, and since I had asked for government aid, I felt some personal responsibility in seeing the thing through. But it was rather saddening to see thousands of people, and there were thousands of them, suffering and dying and little we could do about it. We finally stopped it and it never did become epidemic at the military installation here. While it was very severe in the city of Wichita Falls, the trainees out at Call Field were not affected very much by it.

—*Walter Cline*

Getting Groceries to Caddo

When we made the longest stay in Texas was when we came here in 1918, right after the armistice, to Caddo, Texas. Well, that was, of course, when the big Burkburnett boom—Burkburnett, Ranger, Breckenridge—boom began. And for two or three years it was on. Caddo was an inland town. There was twenty miles of mud to Ranger, seventeen miles of mud to Strawn, and it was always debatable whether the better way to go was with the hack driver or to go with the man with the automobile. Some figured that you'd have less grief if you went with the hack driver. Well, that's the two methods of transportation in and out, and cost you as much as twenty dollars, and lucky to even get in and out for that.

But at Caddo there was a very unusual thing to happen. In those days, of course, there was just trails; there weren't even good dirt roads, and we had a very sloppy, wet winter, which is a matter of history with about everything connected with Ranger and Caddo. Just a ranch trading post was all Caddo was before this oil thing started. And I presume there was fifteen thousand people out there during boom. Of course, in those days where they had oil, they had a camp. Everybody lived close to his work. Transportation wasn't like it is now, where they can drive thirty-five or forty miles and do a day's work and drive back. Most of them lived where they could walk, with a dinner pail in their hand. There was easy ten thousand people at Caddo, in the winter of '18, '19.

When all this population rushed in there, all this drilling equipment came in and all the people come there, the cheapest way a groceryman could get bread from Fort Worth was by parcel post, and all the groceries that they would order—send it parcel post in as large parcels as would be permissible, because it was a dollar a hundredweight, freight out there. Either from Strawn or Ranger it was a dollar a hundred, a cent a pound. The parcel-post rates were cheap then. In the closest zone that there was—why, it was the cheapest way to get light groceries, and the cheapest and quickest way to get them out there from Fort Worth.

Finally the poor fellow that had the Star [mail] route—why, when he took it, of course, was in the old days, when he could carry three or four passengers to help pay out. He carried passengers along with the mail, and just in a hack. Well, it finally got to where a team of horses or a truck wouldn't handle it. Then he had to give it up; he threw it up entirely.

Here the Ranger post office was stacking full of stuff, and finally a guy took it on, and he had four or five trucks, mind you, running down there to try to do it, and he went broke. The Ranger post office would just get stacked full.

Then the ice situation is another goodie, for that area up there. They used to ship ice out from Fort Worth, and it came to Ranger and was hauled out from there. In the hot summertime those mule skinners and truck drivers that brought it out, they'd throw a canvas over it. And it took some time to go that twenty miles in those days, and by the time they got it to Breckenridge, some of those big old wide cakes was about six inches thick. But still it was three hundred pounds and three dollars a hundred, nine dollars for a cake of it. And you'd go down for a hundred pounds of ice, they'd go across it and take a third of it, and there you are. And of course the darn thing would, instead of a hundred pounds, weigh about thirty-five, but still it was a hundred pounds of ice.

—E. P. Matteson

Food and Water

You couldn't get laundry done; it was impossible to get laundry done. We'd just wear our khakis till we couldn't stand them any longer, and throw them away and put on some new ones. You never got any laundry done. There wasn't any place to get it done; there wasn't any water to get it done with.

Meals in those oil-field boardinghouses—of course, they just had big long tables and, boy, they'd rush in there and sit down, and if you was lucky enough to get a seat, all right. And if you wasn't you just didn't get anything to eat. The food was pretty fair. Most of those boardinghouses fed pretty good. It was good substantial food, nothing fancy about it, but most of it was pretty good food. Some of those boardinghouses wasn't very well run, but for an oil-field boom town like that, why most of the food was pretty good. You got worse food in the cafés than you would in those boarding-houses. It was practically impossible to get decent food in those cafés. And you'd go in the café and sit down and order, if you got a chance to sit down. You'd order your meal and if you ordered some kind of a roast or meat dinner, no telling what you'd get. But you didn't dare to say a word about it; you just ate it like that was what you wanted. If you said one word about it they'd just grab it up and give it to somebody else and tell you to get up and get away from there. They didn't want to fool with you at all.

In those cafés, even in Wichita, when you went into a café you paid to get out of there, regardless of whether you ate or not. You had to have a check and pay the cashier something before you got out of that café. There wasn't any walking out and saying, "I'm going somewhere else to eat," because they didn't know whether you ate and was pulling out to get by or not. You just had to have a check to get out of there; and they had a little two-by-four alleyway for you to go out at, and it got to where that if us three went in there and ate, why I couldn't pay the check unless the two guys were right with me, and I positively said I'm paying for these two men. The best way to do it was for each man to have a check.

In most of those places, they was two great big old burly guys standing one right on each side with a big old six-shooter on; and brother, you didn't want to argue with them. That Mecca Café, I remember there in Wichita Falls—they had three cafés there, and I ate quite a bit there at the Mecca Number Two when I could get there. And I knew one of those old boys in there that was waiting a table and counter, and he would give me icewater. You would get one glass of water with your meal, and if you didn't tip him fifty cents—why, you didn't get any more water. If he knew you—I ate there so much that he got to know me pretty well—why, he'd give me more water. Of course, I would usually tip him pretty good; but those, those hashers in those cafés—good night! They made far more money in tips than they did in their salary, and they all drew good salaries. They made plenty of money, those old boys did.

You take an old boy that was right up on his toes in those cafés, and waiting on a lot of people and just halfway courteous to them —why, he made—why good night! It wasn't anything to give him a couple of dollars. Lot of guys would give him a couple of dollars just for all the icewater they could drink, you know. Water was at a premium down there; it was impossible to get any. It cost you a dollar to take a bath in those old bathhouses and they'd give you fifteen minutes, and fifteen minutes was all you got. If you wasn't out of there, why this big old buck nigger'd come along and jerk the stopper out of the tub and tell you to "Get out, bud." Some of us boys got to going out to the swimming pool. We'd go out to the swimming pool and get a bathing suit and we'd run and dive in, just caked with dirt. Well, they got on to that, then they wouldn't let us go into the pool. They barred us from that.

—*Jack Knight*

BOOM-
TOWN
LAW

5

Among the thousands that flocked in to new oil towns, there would of course be the workmen necessary to build the rigs, drill the wells, erect the storage tanks, and lay the pipe lines, and the supervising personnel to direct them. There would be promoters, honest and dishonest, lease brokers, boardinghouse keepers, clerks, waiters, dishwashers, bank tellers—that is, the people who were needed to maintain a minimum of services necessary for existence. Also there would be saloonkeepers and in prohibition times bootleggers, gamblers, prostitutes and pimps, and a large assortment of outright criminals: thieves, holdup men, professional gunmen, narcotics pushers, and representatives of all other categories of crime. The Klondike had set a precedent, created a folklore of roughness, and there was at times a kind of pride in saying that a new oil town was as bad as the Klondike, or worse.

The existing police force, which might consist of only a county sheriff and a few deputies, would be utterly unable to maintain order. It would have to be augmented. Applicants for police positions would include sadistic men who took pleasure in wielding club and gun, greedy men looking for a quick way to make a dollar, and criminals allied with the very people they were supposed to arrest and bring to justice. There was little time for proper screening. Sometimes the local government fell into the hands of the criminals. Opportunities for police graft exist everywhere, but they were especially prevalent in the boom town. The gamblers and prostitutes, for example, might be fined periodically and the proceeds would go to the police and magistrate as fees. It was important that they stay in business. Or protection money might be extorted and one bootlegger assured a monopoly. Robberies and murders would become frequent. Individuals would arm to protect themselves. Vigilante groups would be formed, including the Ku Klux Klan. Good government and reform movements would be organized. But a municipal administration might be overthrown only to be succeeded by a worse one.

Time after time, the state would eventually intervene. State police, in Texas the Rangers more often than the militia, would be sent. Local officers would be suspended and often placed under arrest. There would be a wholesale exodus of undesirables, sometimes under Ranger supervision, sometimes before the Rangers arrived. Illegal establishments would be raided, arrests would be made, convictions would be obtained. Law and order would be restored, and the Rangers would be withdrawn. Sometimes they were sent back, but usually the knowledge that they might return exerted a strong restraining influence. But more important, by the time all this had happened, the limits of the oil field would have been determined and the boom would be declining, and undesirables would be looking for pickings elsewhere. Perhaps a new field would already be opening and history would repeat itself.

Beaumont was the first real victim of boom-town lawlessness. Jefferson County had a sheriff and constables; Beaumont had a small city police force. The officers in both cases were accustomed only to the kind of crime to be encountered in a respectable little southern town.

Beaumont

Well, law and order—why, during those days, they didn't have it. Everybody was his own boss, and everybody done as he pleased, and humanity was plumb tore up at that time. I can't realize right now that anything could have went on as it did in those days. Everybody was—didn't have no respect for one another, and it was just go and come—just a bunch of boomers, what you might say. Here today and gone tomorrow. And, of course, we had a lot of killing, a lot of mystery going on that nobody's ever found anything out about it, I suppose, at that time. But, as far as I know, why, I was a kid, and I tried to make an honest living, and I didn't have much time to mix up with those kind of people.

Gambling and everything else going on. It destroyed the whole country at the time. It lasted—let me see—Spindletop, Sour Lake, Batson, and Humble and Saratoga—I think after those four or five booms things went to settling down.

—Max T. Schlicher

I have since been through many oil booms, but during the heyday of Beaumont, it was undoubtedly the most congested place I have ever seen. Attempt if you may to visualize a little town of about nine thousand population, trying to absorb fifty thousand uninvited guests. Lawlessness and highjacking became rampant. Mayor Flincher hired an able officer from New Orleans, and he soon had matters under control. If my memory does not serve me badly, for nine consecutive mornings a floater—a dead man—was found in the muddy waters of the Neches River. Later a bartender and a Negro porter were charged with being responsible for these murders.

There were men in there, the same as I was, maybe workmen, but generally the men who were killed and murdered were fellows

who had flashed some roll of money. A man would come into this
bar and would flash a roll of money. The bartender would put a
knockout powder in it; the Negro would hold him out in the back,
and during the early morning hours they would take him and throw
him over in the Neches River.

—H. P. Nichols

One time there was quite a great deal of shooting here. Some of
the saloons where the men were killed, some of the policemen got
in, some of the deputy sheriffs got in, shooting at each other and
those things. That was quite common, quite frequent those days.
They had a whole lot of killings here and it was pretty tough for
two or three years after I came here. Ralph was a good sheriff. He
kept order pretty well, exceptionally well, I think, under the circumstances. He had some good men with him. Occasionally they'd get in
some man that wasn't any good. The same thing on the police
force. Occasionally they'd get somebody that would go haywire and
give them a lot of trouble.

We had no trouble with the Negro and whites. The niggers
at that time here were just as—the old southern way. In other words,
they considered theirselves to go to the back door. They didn't come
to the front door and they didn't give any trouble. Later years occasionally they'd go in, whites would go in and burn some of the
Negro houses and those things. At that time there wasn't much
trouble here with them.

[Saloons] were very, very numerous. On Pearl Street in two
blocks there, there was one, two, and around the corner was two
more. A block down below was another one and across on the Sunset Court was two saloons. One on Orleans and one in between
there. And outside of town all the grocery stores sold beer and wine
without a license and there was saloons scattered all over town. All
the suburbs had saloons in them. Some of them were not well
ordered and the Sunday propositions here—they were selling whiskey on Sunday and there was quite a bit of trouble about that. In
fact, one man was killed on account of it on Sunset Court.

I didn't see it and I heard it. The only thing that I know of is
the man was walking on Sunset Court and there was, I think it was
a bartender, I believe, stepped out of the back door of the saloon and
killed him as he passed coming up there, I believe. That's about the

only definite one I know of that happened directly in a saloon, with a saloon.

The red-light district was open and covered quite a territory at that time. When I first came here they had much better houses than they did later on. I think that was because of the out-of-town money that was here, you understand. During the boom a great many of them. Some nice houses were built, but they later either burned down or else those nice two-story houses were finally taken over for something else.

And then they were segregated into a smaller district and they kept them pretty well in the district. If they got out and moved around at all they'd arrest them—take them back and put them in. They kept them pretty well confined to the district for many, many years.

They [Beaumont people] were bitter against it but they tolerated it, and it was understood that it was practically, you might say, legalized in that as long as they stayed in the district they didn't bother them. But if they got out of the district, well, they did. The ministers and church people tried to close it time and time and time and again and they finally succeeded in closing it completely, and they scattered out then all over Beaumont. Took up their residence in apartments, especially downtown apartments.

[Venereal disease] was awful. It was really terrible. Both men and women. They didn't have much treatment at that time. They used common old potassium permanganate, different forms of different solutions, and had preparatory remedies of all kinds. Advertised it all over the country and all the downtown restrooms and toilets all over the country, all over every place had big signs up there printed, you know, medicine for venereal diseases. Some of them were no good at all, of course. They were just out to get their money. But the main thing at that time was irrigation with the potassium permanganate and certain drugs they gave internally.

They helped some, but they had no antibodies at that time. And some cases resisted treatment absolutely. Didn't do it, and when it was a female it was just too bad in those days for the female. They practically were ruined for life when they once contracted the disease. We could handle it very well, got rid of the acute condition all right, but there's nearly always some chronic condition left there. Men and women suffer in later years from the cause of it.

The public in those days were not well informed. The young

men thought it was smart to contract the venereal disease. They'd brag about it. They didn't know what it meant in the future. They thought that they were cured, you understand. And even the same thing with syphilis. They didn't know. They didn't know what was coming later. They'd go and take treatment and get over the acute attack and their tertiary symptoms come later, you understand— and consequently they have all kinds of disease and die young.

It was pitiful the way some of them, there was many and many in those days, a lot of patients of mine that never knew how or where they ever contracted the "looies." Young men, some of them paralyzed before they knew that they'd ever had it, before they ever knew they'd been exposed to it. Some very prominent men didn't know that they'd ever been exposed to it, and it was hard for them to believe when the diagnosis was finally made that they had contracted the disease. That's not only here in Beaumont but that was all over the world at the time there about them, and they called it the "pock."

—*Dr. D. W. Davis*

Beaumont Policemen

There was about eighteen saloons on my beat, and it was three-quarters of a mile around it. And that was my job. Well, we had all kinds of ups and downs and all kinds of troubles and trials. There was eleven men killed on my beat there in nine months, various ways. I found one one night with his head crushed where a big heavy truck had run over it, just mashed his head flat. Another one got burned up in a saloon, over at the Stallion Saloon. Another one was looking in the window watching a bartender count his money, and he looked up and saw him. Just picked up a little gun and shot, went right on counting his money.

Well, we had about, I guess, four hundred of those women on my beat, besides the saloon men. And of course, when they get drunk they're troublesome, always. But they knew whenever I told them anything, told them orders, they'd better take them.

Now, I went down there one night. The old man, Langham, that is, the mayor, said, "I don't want that gal to play after twelve o'clock, Saturday night." I went down there and there was two of them playing in there. I asked them, "Didn't I tell you what the old man said about playing?"

"Oh," she says, "I'm not going to pay no attention to you and that old man so and so." Says, "We'll just teach you and him a lesson."

"All right, all right."

"What are you going to do?"

I says, "I'm going to call the wagon and send you to jail."

She says, "You better wait and find out who's in here."

I says, "I don't care who's in here. I'm going to be the policeman of the morning anyhow."

She hollered for the chief and he was in there, and he said to her, "What's the trouble?"

She says, "That smart aleck's going to lock me up, me and sister."

"Well," he says, "he's the policeman. I ain't got a thing in the world to do with it." Says, "He's following out instructions." He says, "I haven't done nothing, have I, Bill?"

I says, "No, sir, you haven't."

So then she says, "Well, I'll just wait and see." Then they called, "Oh, Emmy, come here." That was the mayor pro tem.

He says, "Hello, Bill."

I says, "Howdy, Mr. Emmet. How are you?"

"All right."

She says, "Say, that smart aleck's going to try to lock me up."

"Well," he says, "if you been doing like you've been doing, I don't think he'll *try* it." Says, "I'm satisfied he'll *do* it."

"Ain't you going to stop him?"

"Why, no. He's the policeman down here. I'm not." Says, "I haven't done anything, have I, Bill?"

I says, "No, sir."

I locked them up. The next morning the judge asked me what was the charge. I told him, told him they'd learn me and that old son of a so and so a lesson.

He says, "Well, girls, I'm going to give you a lesson. Two hundred dollars. Call the next case."

I had a diamond crook to come in there on the beat one night. And there was a little Indian woman told me that he was there and to watch him.

He was going to get the landlady drunk and rob her. Well, our place was set behind a curtain right at the head of her bed. She went to bed. In about thirty minutes, why, she was snoring so you could have heard her all the way to the depot. He raised up and looked at her, just as though to listen, eased out of bed, and he had a pair of rubber shoes. He slipped them on, eased around and got the keys from under her head, opened where the diamonds was. She had about fifty thousand dollars' worth. Had them in a little sack, and when he got the diamonds out, I just opened the curtain and says, "Buddy, just hold your hands still now; don't move, because I don't want to kill you."

He offered me what he had, about fifty thousand dollars' worth already. He offered me that to let him run and not try to kill him. If I'd shoot and not kill him, he'd give it to me. I told him, I says, "No, I'm going to let the court take its course."

I went down there one night and there was a little French girl in one of them cribs. She was crying. I asked her what was the matter and all she could say was, "Mr. Policeman." I went out and saw the bartender. I says, "Charlie, I want you to go around there with me. That French girl's in trouble and I don't know what's the matter with her because I can't talk her language and she can't talk mine."

He went around there and told me this fellow had took her up in New Orleans and told her he had a job for her that would pay her two hundred fifty, three hundred dollars a month. So I said, "All right. Get your clothes." She got her clothes, and I took her to the hotel. "And now," says I, "you give me your papa's phone number, his address and everything." She give it to me and I went down to the phone and called her daddy.

He says, "I'll be there, I'll be there."

So the next night when I went down to work, there was a train in from New Orleans. I saw a very genteel-looking old fellow coming down the street. He walked up to me and said, "How do you do, sir?"

And I says, "How do you do?"

He says, "I'm looking for a policeman called Will Armstrong. Do you know him?"

I says, "Yes, I know him. This is him right here."

And he says, "I talked to you last night over the phone about my girl."

"Yes, I know it."

He says, "Where is she?"

I says, "Well, I've got to go another block this way. You come with me and I'll take you down to where she's at." So we went around the block. I finished up and walked back to the hotel where she was and I says, "Now, she is in room so and so. You get the key—or she's got the key. It's locked. You go ahead now."

"Oh," he says. "No, you come too."

I went with him. He knocked on the door. He says something in French and she says, "Papa." And she opened the door and he went in and talked to her. And she told him what I'd done, and how it happened and all.

The old man says, "Well, young man, I don't know what I can do for you. Just anything that I can do for you, why, let me know. And if you ever come to New Orleans, come to my house and you're at home, just like you was my boy."

I thanked him kindly, and I heard from the old man one time after that. They were getting along all right. He wanted to know if I was ever coming to see him. I never answered the letter because I knew I wasn't going.

They had what we called a honky-tonk down there. The old house is still there. They had about fifteen or twenty girls. They'd have a little show, and the girls were what they called beer jerkers. They'd get a fellow up in a little booth they had there and bleed him for all they could, sell him keys to their room. I know there was a man down there one night and I told him, I says—we called him "Nigger"—I says, "Nigger, why don't you go on home? Throwing your money away here."

"Oh," he says, "I'm going to spend the night with my girl."

So I passed him about four o'clock in the morning and he was sitting on the steps, the foot of the stairs coming out of that house. I says, "Nigger, ain't you going home at all tonight?"

"No," he says. "She'll be down directly."

"Why," I says, "I saw her and her man beating a retreat three o'clock this morning."

And consequently I had to give him a quarter to buy his breakfast with so he could go back out there and go to work.

There was two women that I know of—I wouldn't care to call their names because their people were some of the best people in Beaumont. I went down there one night and she was crying, this woman was, and I asked her what was the matter, and she told me.

"Well," I says, "don't you cry no more. I'll try and straighten you out." I went and brought a fellow down there and he took her out, and she made him the finest home you ever saw. Just made him a fine home and wife. And they had a respectable life after that.

And she was well educated too, this woman was. I never saw or heard her use a smutty word, never saw her drink any. She was just a nice woman.

I went around one night and there was a big half Indian, half Dago gal in one of them houses. And she had a knife. It was sharpened just like a razor. And I says, "Emma, what are you going to do?"

And she says, "I'm gonna to kill every whore in that house. I'm going to catch them as they come by and cut their heads off just as they come by me."

I says, "Come on now, Emma. I want to talk to you awhile."

"All right," she says. "I'll go with you."

She pulled the door to on us. We went out there and I says, "Don't you want a drink, Emma?" I always carried a bottle of knock-out with me.

"Yes, I believe I will."

I give her that and in five minutes, why she was just dead to the world. So I went to open the door and said, "Now, all of you go ahead. When she gets up, she'll be over it all," I says.

And she didn't wake up until next morning about seven or eight o'clock. I went down and she says, "Will, what was I doing last night?"

I says, "You had a butcher knife there and was going to kill them women. What was you mad about?"

Says, "I don't know. I was just mad."

—*Will Armstrong*

Carrie Nation

I recall at one time, just across the street from the American National Bank there was a Catholic church. And then a little farther down the block there was a saloon. One night Carrie Nation was here and she had given her lecture. I was an usher in the theater. I used to usher to get to go to see the shows free. She was coming back down to a boardinghouse that she was staying at, which was located right in this neighborhood. And I had her grip and she darted into one of those saloons and I just put her grip down on the sidewalk and left, went on home. I don't know what she did, I didn't stop to see. But she did not break up anything. She didn't have her hatchet with her. She just went in there and gave them a tongue-lashing. But I didn't stay for it. I put her bag down and left. She was a nice-looking elderly lady, rather stout. And she was quite a character, as everybody knows.

—*Ashley Weaver*

Reception at Batson

I walked across there from Sour Lake. There was three of us. It's about twelve miles across there. We walked to keep from riding on those corduroy roads around there, which would shake you plumb to death. And I got in there—we got in there—almost night, about tired out. I ate supper, and I found a little tent with no floors; had some cots, and right next door to a little flatboard saloon with the gambling house in the back end. I went to bed. All I done was pulled off my shoes. I lay down. I was just dozing off when they started an argument in this gambling house there, and commenced to throwing beer bottles, and started to shooting; and about the second shot must have knocked a hat full of dirt from under my cot. So I come out of there.

And the next morning I started down toward the field, and I saw three fights before I got out on the street. They didn't have any jail yet. There was a huge tree. I think it was burr oak—I am not sure—right out in the middle of the street. So the jailer there—this trusty—put him on that tree there, and padlocked [a chain] around the fellow's neck. That was the jail.

The law over there—there wasn't any law much, you see. The law come over there, and collected what money they wanted, and the persecuting [sic] attorney over there was first cousin of the biggest gambling house, and there was about twenty-five or thirty of them. He walked up and picked up a big handful of silver and some bills, stuck them in his pocket. Well, they didn't say anything; none of it was legal, you know. And they said old [Ranger] Captain Bill McDonald got pretty tough. Captain Bill McDonald—I happened to be there when he came in. I used to know the old man long be-

fore Batson Prairie. I knew him back in '98 in West Texas. Before
the oil field. He was a little dried-up fellow. He stepped out of the
hack there. This sheriff and county attorney was there in front of
this hotel. He asked someone who they were. They told him—a big
crowd around there. He says, "My name is McDonald." Said, "The
state sent me down here." Says, "I want a change made here in the
next twenty-four hours." And says, "You want me to tell you before
this crowd what you gotta do, or would you rather go ahead and
do it?" He [the sheriff] kinda hanged his head, and said he would do
it. So they changed things up there. In other words, Old Captain
just wasn't afraid; he just didn't know what fear was.

They cleaned Batson up, but it was really tough at that time.
There was, I believe, two grocery stores, one drygoods store, and a
drugstore, several restaurants, and nine saloons, and seventeen
gambling houses, about six or seven dance halls.

—Hardeman Roberts

Batson's Prairie

Mr. Brown, who run a saloon on the north end of the main
street of Batson, and he had a friend who was a gambler but stayed
on the south end of town mostly where most of the gambling
was going on. This friend of Mr. Brown's was going to leave, and
he come down one day to bid him good-by. And Mr. Brown asked
him after they exchanged greetings as to how he liked the town. He
said, "What do you think of our place?"

The gambler told him, he says, "I do not say that everybody
here in Batson is a son of a bitch, but I do say that every son of a
bitch is here that could get here."

—James Donohoe

One night, one morning there at Batson they picked up five
fellows that was killed that night. They's layin' around different
places, you know. Some fellow'd knocked 'em in the head. At Sour
Lake it was not uncommon to go down in the morning, any morning, to go down through the oil fields and find somebody that'd
been highjacked and knocked in the head. And it was the same way
at Spindletop, and Humble.

Wide open on gambling and beer joints and saloons. Wasn't no
prohibition then, you know. Old, what was his name? He was district

attorney over there in Hardin County—Ralph. He was up there at the Chicago Fair, somewhere there, and they wired him back to arrest all the gamblers and the whores at Sour Lake and Batson.

And so one Saturday evening there, he give a show. He turned a white whore and a nigger whore out and let 'em fight, and he charged a dollar apiece for all the people who come down to watch it. Make 'em pay a dollar to see this fight, these fights. Had one great big old nigger there. She cleaned up on 'em pretty good. Finally come to a little old black-headed French gal—turned her out with a big old nigger woman. And she give that old nigger gal the worse whuppin' you ever saw anybody git in your life. And it cost you a dollar to see every fight. Well, maybe they'd be eight or ten fights. They'd pull hair and bite. And kick. But boy, that little old French gal, she gave that old nigger mama the awfulest whuppin' you ever saw! And it was funny to us kids, you know.

—Clint Wood

Monday-morning Roundup

There was about thirty-three saloons and beer joints, we called them, operating in Batson. I'll tell you how they operated those places. Now there would be a saloon here, right in the back there would be a vaudeville play, and a dance hall. They had a vaudeville show when they first opened up, and the vaudeville lasted until say till eight o'clock. You buy the ticket at the cigar counter and come in and sit down. They were all in the back. You seen the vaudeville, and right adjacent to that was a dance hall. They either had a brass band or they had a piano, and the fellow played the piano, and there was anywhere from twelve to fifteen girls waiting in there.

Well, you went ahead and you chose your partner and you danced. At the end of that you wanted to have a bottle, and you bought a bottle of beer—you and your partner. You went to your seat and pushed the button, and the porter come back and got your bottles, split one of them, and there would be two straight glasses and a bottle of beer. You give the porter fifty cents. He went back and brought back your change, and give the girl a check for thirty cents. She put that down in her hose—the thirty cents. In other words, it cost you thirty cents to dance a set.

Every one of those places—the girls—every girl was subject to a fine of twelve dollars and eighty cents a week. Well, when they had this roundup there—a lot of these girls were waiting for their trial; the rest were inside or had finished up and had gone. They paid twelve dollars and eighty cents—you might say for living here that week. They fined them that. This saloon [keeper] then come up there, and they paid twenty-five dollars a week for every gambling device he had. If he didn't have a license, he paid twenty-five dollars for that, but it finally became so numerous, so many, you couldn't get to them all in one day with all of us fellows working. We tried to get them all—the landladies, we called them, the ones that owned the houses—and we went down there. We checked the landlady and how many girls she had. If she had fifteen girls—you go out there and paid your fine and fifteen others. It would be sixteen fines that you would owe. We booked her and turned her name over to the justice of the peace. The gambling devices the same way. Went to every place and checked the tables he was running, and let him come up and pay, because we couldn't get to all the people down there. There was some of them that lived off separate to themselves, and it was really a big job—take all day long—the best you could get out of it—to fine all of them, and possibly you missed some of them.

—W. E. Cotton

Texas Rangers

Saloons and stuff like that was built up on the main street of Batson but so many times it was so muddy you couldn't hardly get through it. And it was so overpopulated and so many women, lewd women, bad women, come in there, see. And I have seen them cross from one side of the street to the other, and go up above the old Crosby Bar that was in Batson. They wouldn't have one ounce of clothes on in the world—just like you come into the world. Right across through the rain and through that mud and up the stairs. Of course, drunk, I suppose, or drinking. It was a tough place.

The only thing I can tell you about the Rangers—the Rangers didn't stay there all the time; they would come in and out. But now I'll tell you, when they would come in, they would clean up the place, and it would look pretty decent for a while. Then, the first thing you know, gambling, and women, and everything else, and slaves, and it would be right back to where it was before.

This old judge, I forgot his name, but he would just get his money off of them women, see, and their jail was a big tree with a log chain around it. That was the jail. A tree here and a tree here, and there'd be maybe five, six, seven, or eight men or women chained to that tree. They wouldn't hardly ever chain two to one tree. They would get them far enough away so that they couldn't get together, but that was the jail.

Now, one time I was sleeping in what I called the office, one room off the warehouse. Well, I had hired a fellow that I knew for a long time to fire the boilers because the boilers were setting right there close. "Now," I said, "I'm going to hire you"—he comes from the other field—"because I know you, and I want you to watch me when I am asleep as much as you watch them boilers. And I'm going to tell you one thing, if I ever catch you sleeping, or nodding on this job, you're off; you're going right then, because they're killing too many people around here and I don't want to get killed." At that time I had to have lots of money in my pocket all the time.

I had gone to bed this particular night and the other boys had a bunkhouse over here just fifty or seventy-five feet from that and one of them come in there and woke me up. His name was Jim Nebbe. He's dead now. And he said, "Bert, you got any money?"

I said, "Well, a little, what do you want?"

"Well," he said, "we was a-playing a little poker over there and," he said, "you know, the law come in and got us and fined us twenty dollars apiece."

It wasn't the law, it was just another bunch of kinda highjackers come in and posed as law, and I had to give them, I give them a hundred dollars—they had twenty dollars between them left. And so I give them each one twenty dollars apiece and they went out and give it to them fellows and that's the last ever heard of that. There wasn't no law, there wasn't no court, no nothing. They just took the money and away they went.

—*Bert Stivers*

Robbery at Ranger

I got there before it got so bad. And there was an old lady had rented the top floor of the post office, only a two-story building. It had been a hall, I guess, before, for it was partitioned off into little six-by-eight rooms, just part way to the ceiling. And I got one of them and I kept it until I left Ranger. I was offered three times as much as I'd paid for my room to turn it over to somebody else, but Mrs. Slocomb didn't want anybody else there. She was careful about who she got in. When she found somebody didn't suit her, his rent wasn't renewed.

When the boom got on, there was no place for anything like half the people that come to Ranger and Eastland. I left Ranger before it got quite so terribly bad, just when the flu epidemic was starting there. I come over and drilled on a wildcat well that kept us for eight or ten months, over south of Eastland. In Eastland I saw people who had plenty of money, nicely dressed men and women, both sleeping on board piles, without any cover at all. There wasn't any cover available. On wet nights, things were pretty bad. They didn't stay long, but there was always somebody coming to take their place. The railroad station was full of people sleeping on the floor, and lots of money in their pockets, willing to buy a place to stay, but there wasn't any.

At Ranger, I watched Ranger Lewis operate. A young man come into the restaurant where I was eating my breakfast. He was very roused, and Lewis asked him what was the matter. And he says, "Just got paid today and on the way down I met a couple of fellows that relieved me of it, that's what." Lewis says, "Loan me your dinner bucket." And he was gone about thirty minutes he come back down with a couple a fellows that had tried to rob *him* when he was going back up the railroad. And he says to the young fellow who was still standing there, looking mad, he says, "Are these the fellows?"

"As near as I can tell, them's the birds."

Lewis asked him how much he had. He said he had one hundred and fifty dollars and he reached in the fellow's pocket and counted about a hundred and fifty dollars and put the rest back.

—Clair McCormick

Ku Klux Klan

A fellow'd be way out in them canyons somewhere with his outfit where he brewed it and everything. Of course they'd gang up out in there, sit around there and gamble and drink this beer, home brew. But good whiskey was hard to get ahold of. There's one fellow in there, called him Cleave Barnes, was big, high-powered bootlegger there at Ranger, and done a land-office business when he'd git ahold of some of that good whiskey, brought in there.

Not everybody drank. They was a lot of good decent people in the oil field, lot of good citizens. But as a rule, a boom like Ranger was just a riff-raff class of people that just went from one boom to another; had no regard for the other fellow at all. They just lived a life that was drinking and carousing around and work a little, get enough money to get by on, work a short time. Lot of them didn't work any. Depend on gambling altogether. They'd every once in a while have a feud, break out in shooting scrapes in those gambling places. Fact, it was dangerous for a man to get out at night, decent fellow, lot of places.

It got so bad that a decent woman—it was dangerous for her to get out in lots of places without being insulted. They finally organized the Ku Klux Klan down there in that country. I know there was one fellow—they went up there on the rig floor one night and got him. They'd been after him, been warning him to get out of the country. And he wouldn't go. They went up there and got him one night on the rig floor, taking him off down the road, I guess four or five miles, but they didn't harm the fellow at all. They just took him off and told him what they would do if he didn't leave. So he got out. Never heard anything more from him.

They'd gather and have them meetings around there, have them at nights, put on quite a show. They wore masks when they went out to these regular meetings, but sometimes they'd have a big picnic or something and invite people out. They knew it was a Ku Klux meeting, but they wasn't masked or robed at that time.

They disbanded after the boom was over and all this riff-raff class of people left. Soon as they got the country down there cleaned up around there, why, they accomplished, they figured, their purpose, and they just disbanded and done away with it. The very best class of people, lawyers and doctors and preachers belonged to it.

One time this preacher come in there from Mississippi, and they had a little church, what they called Harmony Baptist Church, and they had an oil well on their property. Been abandoned, hadn't had any church services there for four or five years, but had a right smart of little money in this fund, and this preacher, he come in and reorganized the church and bought him in a bus and went out and gathered the people and carried them to Sunday school, those that didn't have no way.

I remember this same preacher was going to hold a little meeting up above this place where this church I was telling you about, little mission place up there. A bunch of fellows decided they was going to run him out. Wouldn't let him preach there, bunch of them rough, riff-raff class of people. And there was a lot of good citizens there and they wanted this meeting. So myself and another fellow, they got us to go up there—sort of like old pioneer days way back yonder when this country was first settled. We went up there with our guns and stood guard while he preached. Boy, it was rough.

—R. S. *Kennedy*

Highjackers and Bullies

Everybody knows that people in the oil fields, old contractors and drillers and people like that, all used to play a little poker, you know. One night the bunch I associated with, they had a big two-story house leased there and had a lot of rooms in it, bathrooms and everything, you know. They stayed there all time. Well, sometimes they'd have a pretty stiff little game. You could win or lose four hundred to five hundred dollars in a night if you got unlucky or lucky.

Another poker game I wanted to tell you about it. Over in the old Empire field in Oklahoma, we used to play poker once in a while. We had three bunkhouses there—Jerry Kenney and the boys and myself. Had three bunkhouses, and another fellow had a bunkhouse there in the same bunch too. Was four of them there altogether. We used to play poker once in a while there at night, at one of our shacks. This particular night that I was going to tell you about, when the Empire field was going on, there was lots of robbing and highjacking. It was a bad place for highjackers, one of the worst places I ever saw for highjackers.

When I'd stay over at the field there, before sundown I'd get my wood and water all in. I didn't get out after sundown, because you're sure liable to get knocked in the head or highjacked or something.

So one night I was going home to Walters; I lived in Walters and I wasn't going to be there that night. So I did go home, and the boys was having a little game that night—Jerry Kenney and some of the other boys and Frank Pickle was there. Frank was superintendent for the McMan. Before I left, I was the only one in the bunch besides

Jerry that had a six-shooter. I had an old Colt .38. Jerry had a little old .25 automatic that he carried in his vest pocket all the time. So I told him, I said, "I better leave my six-shooter here tonight. You might need it."

I left it and I went on home and that night they was all sitting in the shack, and they had blinds up over the windows, you know, so no one could see in. And way along in the night, about eleven, eleven-thirty maybe, they's sitting there playing poker, and somebody rapped on the door. Jerry was sitting there and he said, "Who is it?"

And the old boy on the outside said, "Jerry Kenney!"

And Jerry told me about it the next day, and said, "When they said that, damn, I knew they's lying. I knew where Jerry was!"

So he got up and told them, told the other boys, said, "Well, boys, get ready. We're highjacked."

Frank Pickle just stepped back between two of the beds and took this old .38 of mine and leveled it down right on the door. And Jerry had his little .25 automatic out, so nervous he couldn't hold it still. And he opened the door and said, Jerry says, "Well, what do you boys want?"

One of them said—there's three of them—he said, "Well, heard you's having a little poker game out here tonight, and we thought we'd come up and play a little with you."

Jerry said, "Yeah, we're having a little game all right, but we don't want no strangers in it, and I think the best thing you boys can do is just go on about your business."

And he just shut the door and they went on. They didn't even try to highjack them, because old Frank Pickle, old Frank was just out of World War I, he had that old .38 Colt in line, and—boy, he was a man that would've used it, too! Don't think he wouldn't! They could see it. He had it leveled right down on them. There was four of them in the bunch; we knew that; we found it out. The other one was probably outside waiting to see what happened, you know.

The next morning I got back over there and they told me all about it. Well, I went uptown and I began to inquire around. I inquired at the hardware store. I knew everybody uptown there, and the old boy at the hardware store told me, "Yeah, that's them high-jackers. I know them. That suits the description. That was them, and they was in here early that night, and bought a bunch of six-shooter shells and a few shotgun shells and stuff and went out. I'm sure that was the guys that's been doing the highjacking around here."

I said, "I want to borrow all the six-shooters I can get." And I borrowed about four or five six-shooters uptown that morning and took them back down the house. The next night when we started to play, I gave everybody a six-shooter.

I sat down over where I was facing the door and I says, "Somebody now raps on that door, I'm laying my old .38 Colt right down beside me. Somebody raps on that door now, you guys on that side of the table better duck, because I ain't going to do much talking. I'm going to let this old Colt talk."

They didn't ever rap on the door and I think that our bunkhouse was the only bunkhouse in the field that never was highjacked. There was lots of highjacking and quite a bit of killing went on there during that boom, and they never did highjack our bunkhouse though. But they come there that night—I'm sure they came to highjack it that night—but they didn't.

And what happened before the Empire boom was near over with, the citizens around there, the roughnecks and drillers all got together, and they knew all them highjackers and gamblers and old women, you know, that was in there, and they rounded up all of them in a bunch. They just went in these boardinghouses and rooming houses and drug them out and kicked them out in the street and rounded them up in a bunch and drove them down the highway. They told them to never let themselves be seen back there again. And they didn't. They left there. They left afoot. I don't know where they went but they didn't come back. That broke up the highjacking and it got to be a pretty decent place around there then.

The last of the old towns where the highjacking and all went on was Borger, Texas. They had the whole nest of them had settled down there in Borger, and I went there a few years after that—two or three years maybe—and they used to be the meanest-looking set of people there I ever saw in my life. At that time all these old highjackers and gamblers and everybody had just settled down there. They just come to the row's end and just settled down there in Borger and went in business. Was trying to make a decent living. They'd been run out of everywhere else and that was the end of the trail. They was the hardest-looking, *meanest*-looking set of old people there in Borger when I first began to go there that I ever saw in my life. You go there now—why, you wouldn't notice any difference from any other place. There's pretty decent-looking people; they've outgrown the thing, you know. Of course, there's a few them old-timers still there.

Around a little old town like that there's always what they call a village tough. He thinks he's tough, you know, but sometimes not near so tough as he thinks he is. My boys tangled up with him one night, and I had one old boy with me that was pretty tough himself. They came up to the hotel where I was, and they asked me, said, "Cotton, you got a six-shooter?"

And I said, "Yeah, I got one. My Colt's upstairs."

They wanted to borrow it and I said, "What do you want with it?"

They told me about the row they'd had with this old boy, this village tough down there at a tent show that was in town. They was going back down there and have it out with him. I said, "No, you don't want to do that. I ain't going to let you have my six-shooter. You'll go down there and get in trouble; may kill that old boy or git yourselves killed. You just don't want to have that kind of trouble. Just forget about it."

It wasn't but a few days after that till two of my friends, Tip Yarman and Jim Daniels, moved a rig in there to Currie, just south of Richland there, and was staying at the same old hotel where I was staying. Jim Daniels was the fastest-fighting little fellow that I ever saw in my life, and the *best* fighter I ever saw in my life. He wasn't very big, but he was a fighting fool.

His boys was in the pool hall. This village tough owned the pool hall there. Jim's boys was in the pool hall playing pool up there one night, and there was another kid in there that they didn't know. This village tough had been picking on this kid, kicking him around, slapped him a time or two maybe. Jim Daniels wasn't there himself, but he walked in pretty quick, and this village tough told him, he said, "I understand that this boy's with you."

And Jim said, "No, he's not with me. I never seen him before in my life that I know of; but he can git with me goddam quick." And he meant it too. He didn't have any trouble anyway. Didn't even have a fight. If they had, wouldn't been hard for me to figure out which one would've won.

—J. T. (*Cotton*) *Young*

Life in the Borger Boom

In that time living conditions in this town were something. There was tin shacks grew up all over town. Bed cots rented for a dollar and a half, dollar to a dollar and a half, and they was rented eight hours, on an eight-hour basis, and you got up and your eight hours was over, and somebody else took the cot; that's the way it was run. And the walls was so thin that when you had the dust storms, it was a pitiful situation in here.

The first jail in this town was a chain stretched between two trees, and when they arrested anybody, they just locked them with their leg around this chain, and just locked them on there. I went after my driller one night, a fellow by the name of George Miller. He didn't show up for work and I figured George had got a little too much Borger hootch, and I went down there and it was the funniest thing I ever saw. He was laying down there on his back asleep, between two of the blackest Negroes that I ever saw, laying under a tree. I woke him up and he said, "I told you you ought to let me go to work." But they fined him seventeen dollars and fifty cents anyhow. The law at that time was very bad. Hutcheson County at one time had fifty-six murders. They had one conviction in three years.

At that time, this town was infested with these prostitutes, [and] these P.I.'s, and that's men that these prostitutes keeps up. And they treat these women, some of them, mostly like dogs. I guess that's the way they got them into this prostitution. These guys deal in white slavery in men and women. There was numbers of these people in this town at that time. They did make a surprise raid every once in a while, but it never did amount to nothing. The law was getting paid off; the sheriff that was elected was getting paid off. At that time, people didn't seem to be interested in government. They thought the town would be here probably a couple years, three years, four years; get outside and we'll be gone, we don't care anything about it; and the honest people mostly lived out in camps, they didn't live in the town. The only honest people that lived in town and made their living was some merchants who'd come into this town, with the idea of maybe staying.

—*Earl Snider*

Incident at Burkburnett

I know of one case where one of the guards of one of the companies was trying to catch a man that was doing highjacking at nights. He'd knock people down and take their money. So he did his arm and hand up in a false splint with a pistol in it, and he deliberately had a big roll of bills in his pocket, and he went into a little restaurant where he'd followed this man at night and ordered coffee. And he made a display. He just took a big roll of bills out of his pocket and removed the rubber band with his teeth, then he pulled a bill off of that roll with his teeth, and then got the man behind the counter to put the rubber band back on and he put that back in his pocket. And when he left, it was a very short time when he went around a rooming house, just an old oblong straight-walled, wooden shack, tin roof, that this highjacker told him to put up his hands. And he just aimed that splint and let go with a pistol and that was the end of that highjacker.

—*A. B. Patterson*

Robbed and Robbers

We had a lot of experiences in building that doggone [telephone] line and camping in there. There was two tents of us. And one night, about two o'clock in the morning, why something woke me up, and there was a guy climbing, coming in the front door, the flap. Had the flap open on this tent, and there was one of the boys sleeping right next to the flap and he had a gun in his cot, but nobody else did. There was eight of us in this tent.

That guy just got right up on top of him with his knees and stuck a gun in his head and he told him to stick his hands out and stick them out empty. So he got this gun, and he lined us up there in the tent, and it was kind of comical to watch him. He just started throwing the covers back on those cots. Directly he'd come to that old boy's billfold, see, and he'd pick it up and stick it in his pocket. He got about eleven hundred dollars off that bunch, that night. Always hit just after payday. He got about eleven hundred dollars off us. I was paying all the expenses of this group, see; and the day before I had about four or five hundred dollars. But I'd got into some hard luck over there and I had to spend it all, and I only had about three or four dollars. And he tore my cot up—oh, he never did find it—and he sure tore my cot up like a sow's bed.

He knew, that guy knew. I'm sure that it was the guy that had been working with us a short time before that. He quit, see, because he knew where that gun was, and he knew that I should have some money. He kept looking at me, and searching my cot, but he never did call me by name. I looked for him to. He knew that I should have some and he never did find it.

He was masked and there was another one with him who never did come in. He just stuck his head in the tent once, but he never did come on the inside. Those guys would watch those camps, and when payday come, why then they'd rob them. There was one group of fellows over there that worked for some company that they robbed them about three different times. And one night they came in and was going to highjack them, and one old boy just rolled off his cot down between them, and when this guy walked up the aisle between the rows of cots, crowding the boys back in the other end of the tent, he raised up and grabbed him. And come to find out it was a woman. She admitted that she had robbed them before.

That was in the wintertime, and it was cold and muddy and everything was in an awful mess. And they just stripped her naked, and took her downtown, and just threw her out in that mud, right out in the middle of main street right there in Burkburnett. They didn't abuse her, that is, I mean, beat her up or anything, after they found out it was a woman. They just took her down there and threw her out. There wasn't any law; you couldn't turn anybody over to the law because there wasn't any. They got even with her that way, you see.

—*Jack Knight*

WOMEN

IN

THE

OIL

FIELDS

6

Women followed the booms, and for them the hardships were greater. At best, they could find a shotgun shack to live in or a tent with a wooden floor. The less well-off camped in wagons or bedded down in the shelter of trees, and often suffered from lack of food, medicine, medical care.

These were the legitimate followers—the wives, sisters, and daughters of oil-field workers. Because the towns were too rough, these women had to live out in the fields, often in the shadow of the derrick, always in the danger that the wind would blow in a miasma of deadly gas from a well blowing wild. In spite of the hardships,

these women carried on life as best they could, in a tradition long
the heritage of American pioneer women.

There were also the questionable followers, the "oil-field doves"
who set up their rackets and trades, the Six-Shooter Kates, the
Mooches, and the countless others who left their real names behind
and acquired the names that would make them anonymous in boom
towns and later.

Their stories are told, sometimes in the trivialities of oil-field
life, more often in accounts of survival or death.

Mrs. Hamill's Washpot

That washpot was bought in the early days of our marriage, and
it washed the clothes of our children all through Spindletop. It
was the pot that boiled the water. Mrs. Hamill used that pot to boil
water to wash the oil off the boys during the days that we was putting the gate valve on the well. We still have that old washpot here,
and, while it's quite a wreck, we value it very highly. But it's the only
relic of the Lucas well I suppose a person could swear was used on
the Lucas well. While it was not used on the well, it was used at our
house to heat the water for us to bathe in after we had the oil off us
with towsacks. We first rubbed the rough oil off with sacks or cloth
of different kinds, because you couldn't wash it off. And we would
rub that oil off of us. And then, after we'd rubbed it off, we would
bathe in warm water or hot water as we could stand it. And the old
washpot and two or three other vessels was used to do that. Mrs.
Hamill was the one that boiled the water. Wood fire out in the yard.
Everything was wood then.

It wasn't too safe for respectable women. It wasn't safe for them
to go around these different places in Spindletop and in parts of
Beaumont even, after the bulk of people got there, working people
and different—that follow such a thing. It wasn't safe for a woman
to be out by herself hardly at all. All kinds of vulgar remarks would
be made and cast at her and so on and so forth.

—*Curt G. Hamill*

Batson's Prairie Wife

Meat was very cheap. Steaks and most any kind of beef or pork was about from eight to ten cents a pound and we could buy black bear and venison over the block at the meat counters or from this traveling meatman. I bought one bear roast and I didn't care for it. It was very sweet meat and very dark. We didn't care for the flavor of it so we never bought any more bear meat but we had quite a lot of venison and then a little later we didn't have to buy venison because there was a boy living right across the street from us and he would go out in the woods and kill a deer and just cut it in two and bring the hind quarters home, the best part of the deer, and we had plenty of venison without buying it. And that was the way we got our meat when we first went to Batson.

We were right on the edge of the Big Thicket. We would go down, but the alligators were so bad, and if we'd get into those big palms, oh, they were ten and fifteen feet high from the ground up to where the palm fronds would start, and we wouldn't dare to go into them because if an alligator would get after us, we couldn't get away. And they were very thick. The big alligators were thick there.

We've seen men coming out of those thick, piney woods down around the water with big flannel-mouthed moccasins, I believe they were called, and they would have a rope tied around their neck and I don't know, they would be eight and ten feet long—just huge things. I don't remember how large around they would be but they'd just tie a rope around them and drag them back of their buggies. I don't remember of anyone having been bitten while we were there.

Mosquitoes were terrible. We had to have a mosquito bar over our bed, just a regular canopy, and then at night before we would go to bed, we would put a smoke under the bed and let it smoke good and shake the mosquito bar good before we pulled it around the bed and then usually we would use just a little kerosene and rub it all over our bodies and then about midnight, we'd get up and smoke again and get all the mosquitoes out from the bar. They'd be small when they'd hit the bar and come through. Some people just used cheesecloth because the mosquitoes couldn't get through the cheesecloth.

The sand fleas were so bad that we had straw matting under Mr. Stiver's desk in his office, when he had the office in the house, and when we'd turn out the light, we could hear the sand fleas hopping around on the straw matting on the floor. And we had an awful time with the children because the mosquitoes and the chiggers were so bad that we'd have to put so much stuff on them at night when they would go to bed, and put them under bars, and they just were so restless because the mosquitoes were terrible.

Just a piece of cloth, and just let it smolder. We had regular pans to smoke with. Then if we sat outside, we had to keep smudges going so that the smoke would be blowing over us all the time, or we couldn't stay outside in the evening after sundown at all.

We just had to use coal oil because at that time they didn't have any kind of mosquito dope. We had to take coal oil and we'd dip a cloth in coal oil and hang it on the head of the children's bed and then draw the mosquito bar round and the smell of this kerosene would keep the mosquitoes away for a while. And you'd get up and change. And then we would put flea powder on the sheets to keep the fleas and chiggers and all the things we had to contend with. I never wanted to go back.

At Batson there wasn't a church there while we lived there. But as I said, we organized a little Sunday school and we just sent around and gathered up all the children and grown folks that we could get to go to this little Sunday school. And we'd have a churchful. We'd have grown folks and children both and they seemed to all be interested.

We built a church. Built a little building. Interdenominational. There was quite a few Catholics but they came right into the services with us—and the same way at Humble. We had a few Catholics there that came right into the services and worked in the church with us. We had all denominations in the church, both places. At Batson we had no instrument at all, just sang from the hymnbooks. We had the Methodist hymnbooks and we all just sang from the Methodist hymnbooks. "Bringing in the Sheaves" was one of them. And we used to sing the old-time hymns because everyone seemed to know them.

We had nothing at all except to get out and collect for our Sunday school and that was the only amusement we had. We didn't have any picture shows or anything like that. No card parties. We'd meet and sew a lot of times. And there was some of the ladies that liked to sew and didn't like to work buttonholes and we'd all get together and the ones who liked to work buttonholes would work buttonholes and we'd spend a very nice afternoon that way and serve refreshments.

I was there one year and I was in Beaumont twice during that time. Mr. Stivers and I drove out to Liberty one time just to see the new railroad when it went through and that was the first railroad we had seen since we were married. And while we were out there we had a little white terrier dog, and we were driving it with our little pony and buggy and we let the little dog out, he was anxious to get out and run, and we left him out and we got into a bunch of steers and they stampeded when they saw that dog.

Mr. Stivers jumped out and grabbed the dog and put him in the buggy and we had to turn and run for our lives to get away from those steers. I guess they hadn't seen a buggy and a horse in so long, and the little dog—they were just pawing the earth, coming right toward us. There must have been two or three hundred. Those big long-horned steers, you know. Real Texas longhorns, and I'll tell you, they were just pawing the earth.

[The roads] were built out of pine logs. They would lay two pine logs parallel and then they would lay split pine logs and lay the flat side down and they were not even bolted down; they were just laid down on these two other logs, and then we drove over the rounding side. It was called the corduroy road, and it really was a corduroy road. We bumped all the way from Batson to Saratoga. It was five miles. The horse just had to walk all the way. And the trees were so thick that they would just strike us in the face. We had to keep our arms up to keep the limbs from striking us in the eyes. And I remember when we were taking his father and mother to Saratoga to put them on the train to go back to Ohio, one limb struck his mother on the face and cut her face. We just had to watch them all the time, the trees were so thick.

We all gathered at the little church, and they also had school in this little church, too. And we had a Christmas tree and everyone exchanged gifts. We had a very nice time at Christmastime. On Thanksgiving Day—our first Thanksgiving after we were married—we decorated the interior of our little house with palm leaves and holly and some kind of red berry—a vine with red berries that we gathered in the woods down near the river, or the bayou, rather. And we had three big turkeys and a fruitcake and a white cake, and I made a fruit dish out of a meat platter. I put a wire handle to it and covered it, and we had all kinds of fruit on our fruit dish and all kinds of homemade candy and entertained all of Mr. Stivers' men and their wives and children at a big Thanksgiving dinner. And we had the moss that grows on the trees. We draped it around the rafters because there was no ceiling in the house and it was just plain rafters, just the shell of a house, just a shack. But we made it look beautiful.

At that time we didn't have any fireworks, but after that on Christmas they always had their fireworks, just like the Fourth of July here. They always shot off their fireworks on Christmas Day. But the first Christmas we were there they didn't have any fireworks.

We had to get a doctor from either Liberty, Saratoga, or Beaumont, and sometimes it would be hours before the doctor could get there. And in many cases, if it was a mother giving birth to a child, the child would be born and some of the neighbors would be with the mother, and take care of the child before the doctor got there. I know two of my children were born the same way. I had to call a neighbor each time because the doctor couldn't get out. He only had to come two miles, but the roads were very bad, and we called him and he couldn't get there in time. So I called a neighbor each time and the baby was taken care of before the doctor got there, and they are living yet today, doing fine.

There's the colored people around there. They were very superstitious. I know my oldest child had a bad earache and I tried everything and I couldn't ease the pain in his ear, and there was an old colored man by the name of Smokey and he was a muleskinner—took care of and drove mules for Mr. Hollifield, across the street from us—and he came over to my door and said, "Mrs. Stivers, if you will take just a little wisp of my wool and put it in his ear it will stop his earache." And I said, "Well, Smokey, I'll try it, because I've tried everything." And I took a little wisp of his wool and placed it in his ear and he went to sleep and his earache stopped. And the one old colored woman that used to work for me, she told me whenever I was in trouble in any way, or if either of my children were ill, to take an egg and bury it in a wet place and if it was some place where the egg would be wet and decay quickly, whatever the trouble was would go away. Well, I never tried that.

Forrest Bottomfield, who caused the fire at Spindletop, when he couldn't get work there, he decided that he would try to make money some way, so he took the crude oil, put it up in little two-ounce bottles, and went out and sold it at two dollars for a two-ounce bottle. And that was supposed to be a TB cure, a cure for tuberculosis, and he sold many a dollar's worth that way.

I don't know of anything else [uses of oil] for poultices or anything like that. I don't remember of any. I know they used to use it to clear dandruff. They'd put crude oil on the hair to cure dandruff and that would really do that.

A lot of the older colored people had been living there for years. They just come every morning, four or five colored women would come to our door asking for work, wanting to do washings, and they carried their tub of water on their head and a bucket of water in each hand. We had to carry wash water because there was no wells. And we had to carry our drinking water and then carry the wash water from the pond out in the field where it would rain. And they would go and dip the water out of this pond and fill their tub half full, and then they would get their two buckets full and set the tub on top of their head and squat down and pick up a bucket in each hand and walk just as steady and never drop that tub off of their head and carry it for half a mile.

I kept a colored woman all the time. I kept one to take care of the children, old colored mammy and she was so good to the children, and then we could just pick up colored people any time, because they would just come by the house all the time asking for work.

They would come and work a whole day for fifty cents. And the ones that we would keep all the time, they didn't charge over two dollars a week. And, of course, we fed them all the time. All they cared for was fat meat and vegetables and black-eyed peas and bacon, fat bacon, and corn bread.

The colored women didn't want to do their laundry there in the house. They wanted a tub and a bench on the outside. They wanted to do it on the outside and they had a great big iron kettle and they filled that full of water and built a fire around it to heat their water. That's the way they did all their laundry work. Boiled the clothes right in the open in this big iron pot. So everybody had an iron pot for the colored people to heat their water in and they always had their tubs on the bench on the outside.

I don't remember that I went to more than one funeral. It was the funeral of this little baby I was sitting up with and we had to go to Liberty. There was no cemetery at Batson and these people were Catholics and there was no priest in Batson. So we took the baby in a hack and I carried the little casket on my lap in the back seat and it was only about nine miles, but we had to take a lunch because the roads was bad and it took us a long time to get there. And we carried our lunch. And after we found a priest and the baby was buried, then we ate our lunch and drove back. It took us all day to drive it because the roads were very bad.

—Mrs. Bert Stivers

Women at Work

[I never saw] no particular one taking part in drilling or shave-tailing or anything of that kind. If it was, it was only an isolated case of a woman coming on the job to help her husband when he wanted to go to rest or maybe something of that kind. That has happened in one or two instances that I can remember now. I can remember one or two women who ran boilers. But their husbands were working, running these boilers, and the womenfolks would come down and bring him lunch or bring him a change of clothing or something of that kind. And they had been there often enough for him to tell them how to handle the boiler and how to look after it. And he could go home and lie down, or go home and put his clothing on or something of that kind. And outside of that I don't know of anything.

—H. C. Sloop

Death at Batson's Prairie

One thing that impressed me greatly; in fact, it was two things. There was a family living there, and one of the girls was a gypsy. They were from a tribe that had settled over in Beaumont, but they were very strict people though. But the two brothers run a saloon. Well, one of the brothers' child, about seven years old, became sick and died just in a few hours' time. And being friendly with these people, I went up there to sit that night, and the mother—her grief was just something terrible. It was a calm grief; she didn't cry, she just couldn't understand how and why that child had been taken away from her so soon.

We sat up that night with that child, and I remember wringing rags out of soda and salt and putting on her little face, to preserve the features, and washing her little hands and arms so they wouldn't turn black. And then about two o'clock we all got thirsty and we wanted some soda pop. Well, of course, everything was closed, and so, very daring, we went into this saloon. It was closed, and the people owned the saloon [opened up], and we drank soda pop. Well, we just thought we'd committed an awful sin, and we didn't tell it for a long time—just how daring we'd been as to go into that saloon and drink pop at two o'clock in the morning.

The next morning about nine o'clock, here came a wagon and team with this very crude little coffin, just built out of plain pine planks, rough planks, and we'd lined the inside of it with white. And that little body was put in that coffin and then started that long, torturous drive. It seemed farther than it really was. Way back in those piney woods we came to a little plot of ground that just had a rail fence around it, and the grave had been dug there. There was no preacher; there was no singing; there was nothing. Only just the sobs of the mother and the father and the little brothers and sisters that was left. I'll never forget going off and leaving that little body out there.

Another time there was a baby that lived just in front of us, just about a year old, a cute little old fellow, and there were seven or eight children in that family. They lived in a tent without a floor. And this little fellow became sick and that baby died in my arms. I was thirteen years old. Well, that learnt me then never to fear death. There was a beauty in death, just something about it that we should never be afraid. I sat up all night with that baby, and from then on, I have never feared anything. It was just something that impressed a person so, and it just leads you nearer to God, each experience that I have had that way.

—*Mrs. Sam Webb*

A Wife Bereft

His wife and him was good friends of mine. They were here so much at my house. And somebody walked in there and shot him. No, they shot him outside, and he just fell right on his back, and I went to town. I thought I had heard two guns—just enough to tell there was two, and I went by the house where that friend of mine was at, and she didn't know, and she says, "Come on in." I said, "Did you hear the shots?" And she said, "No, I didn't hear anything." She said, "Come on in. We are frying some oysters. Come on in, and let's have some supper."

About that time her little boy came running in and said, "Mama! Mama! Mr. Whitt got shot!" Of course, me and her—all of us—run out there and there he was lying right on his back, and she just screamed and hollered. She had a skirt on herself, and she unbuttoned that skirt—she had it on top of something else—and she pulled it off, and put it under his head. His old pistol was lying there on side of him. I tell you who was night watchman then—it was Hart, Uncle John Hart.

She took the pistol from him and she said, "I feel like killing everybody in Saratoga!" Because they killed her husband, and he took the pistol away from her, and she said, "Oh, carry him to Mrs. Mattie's to lay him out. He just loves Mrs. Mattie." And they brought him up here and laid him out in my front room in there. And kept him all night, and the next day ordered the coffin and taken him over to Beaumont, and they buried him in Beaumont.

—Mrs. Mattie Evans

Saratoga Texas Wedding

Well, nothing to it, except that I went out of my room into the front room and had the justice of the peace marry us, and that was all there was to it. We wanted to do it, and not tell nobody nothing about it or something or other, but they found out about it and pulled a big stunt that night. It wasn't a shivaree, but he went downtown and bought lots of cakes, wine, and junk and stuff, and a whole bunch of people come up here and we all danced around here after they found out, and they said, "Why didn't you let us know?" Just decided we would do it that way.

He sent somebody else to Kountze and got the license and he had it in his pocket. I didn't know he had it. He was sitting there in my room one evening and he pulled out that license and showed it to me, and he went and rang the justice of the peace, and he come on, and it was over in about a minute.

Somebody said that it wasn't a legal marriage 'cause nobody could have witnessed it, but there was an old lady upstairs that roomed right over, and she heard it all, and she told them, but she didn't see it. But it is on the record just the same. I guess it would take three to take the word for it. Nobody saw it but us.

—Mrs. Mattie Evans

Dance-hall Ladies

Well, I tell you what I seen occur one day on a roundup when we rounded them all up, and bring the niggers and whites up there too. Of course the niggers was supposed to stand back, but there was a nigger woman and a white woman who got into an argument. They was both drunk. They called this woman "Swamp Angel" and the white woman was "Jew Annie." Jew Annie and Swamp Angel got into an argument, and they wanted to fight. This officer tried to keep them from fighting, and the county attorney come along—he had gone out to get him a drink of water or something during the court, and they told him about their trying to fight, and he stopped, and he said, "Well, we can settle that. We can settle that," and he said, "Well, now, I'll make you a proposition. Go ahead and fight—stand back—we'll let you fight, and the one that gets whipped pays both fines." And the nigger woman whipped Jew Annie, the white woman, and he said, "All right, you are free to go now. You whipped her."

They would set up a sewing machine, and that was to keep from being—we had a thing down here, if you didn't have any visible means of support, you was a prostitue, and if she come out there, and sew on something once or twice a day, and had a sign there, "Sewing done here," why, you couldn't prove that she was a prostitue.

—W. E. Cotton

Incident at the Pickwick

I remember one instance where a man rode through the Pickwick Saloon. And this Pickwick Saloon was ran by a woman. She was a woman that dressed very much like a cowgirl always. And she was always in the saloon. And she walked up and down in the middle of the saloon; she very seldom sat down. She was advising the men and women who were at the counters. And everybody drank, men and women, children and all that went there. And she always was giving instructions and orders.

Some man rode through the saloon one day and then out the

back door. And she was wanting him to ride through again. Of course, she always kept a couple of guns hung on her, a big one and a smaller one. And then she had several that you couldn't see, somewhere. Anyway, she was always prepared for an occasion of that kind. And he started in somehow or other, and she shot the reins off of his horse and I don't know what all she did, a lot of things like that. But we didn't see that, we just saw afterwards—what she had done, you see. Course he didn't ride through the saloon any more.

—H. C. *Sloop*

Tough as a Boot

Every one of them had a different name and they didn't want to get back home to their own people that they would write home under their own name. They were going under another name. And I want to tell you something, the best hearts I have ever seen in people is in the underworld. I seen prostitutes after they commit suicide and maybe the girl didn't have anything much. I've seen the other women take off their diamond rings and sell them for twenty-five dollars and fifty dollars and help bury this particular woman. And I noticed among good people that seldom you ever see people do that.

I'll tell you about some of the women—some of the women were taking care of their mother back home, and some of them was probably taking care of a baby where a sorry husband had walked out on them, and when you get right down she had a clean heart on the inside of her.

And some of them was tough as a boot and don't you think they wasn't. Some of them would pick your pocket, and they were just as low as they ever got, and others had lots of pride left. Now I know one woman—she was a fine-looking woman and she killed her husband and later married a field man. That woman straightened out and I believe she lived a clean life from then on. He had a woman. It was either kill her or kill him or get killed, and so she beat him to it. But that woman, she turned out. The last I heard of her she was living in Louisiana and the man she married was right up in the money. And it looked like they was getting along fine, and I never knew her to make another bobble after she married him.

—W. H. (*Bill*) *Bryant*

Mooch

There were a notorious woman that I knew lot of times. She was "Mooch" Frank. Mooch was a gambler's—supposed to be his wife. She'd sit up there right with him at all times—he was a crap gambler—at the crap table. And all these places, why they had saloons wide open; that's where this gambling was. And a low bunch was following so that you had to watch them. But this Mooch was a great character. She was a woman that was very pretty at the time when I first saw her in Sour Lake, Texas. Very pretty woman.

The reason she got that name of Mooch was because if any roughneck or pipe liner would get sick, didn't have any money, anything like that, why she'd go out and mooch all the oilmen in the country. Didn't make any difference if he was an oil producer or what, and they'd all give a dollar or a dollar and a half, that's just their natural way; they are all good-hearted men. Even the producers today are just like they was then, they are all good-hearted. . . . They've been up against it themselves several times. They see how it is. Anyhow, if a boy got sick or anything, why Mooch would start out. Wouldn't be long until she'd have a quack doctor there, medicine, and plenty to eat.

Well, Mooch she died in jail in Shreveport, Louisiana. And whenever they heard it, why all oilmen, even the oil producers, were sad. Chipped in and give her a fine burial. She had a heart—a big heart—so they give her a respectful good burial. She was a farm girl, I imagine. Some place in Texas or Louisiana.

—Frank Hamilton

Happy Marriage

The women stayed here [at Corsicana] for years, some of them. Quite a few of them married from there. We had a woman raised here named [Edith Block] and she left here after acquiring a good deal of wealth and moved to Fort Worth. She had an attorney here that looked after her property and business for her. He told me one day that she called him up and said, "Bob, will you be in your office tomorrow?"

He said, "Yes."

"Well," she said, "I'm coming down. I want to talk to you. I've got some business I want to talk over with you."

He said that she came down from Fort Worth the next day and he said, "[Edith] what's on your mind?"

She said, "Well, Bob, I'm fixing to get married. What do you think about it?"

And he said, "Now, [Edith] look," said, "I can tell you about the title to a piece of property, or whether you get good security on a loan, or whether you ought to buy government bonds or buy some stocks. I can give you good advice on this, but when it gets down to you getting married, just leave me out. I don't know what to tell you."

"Oh," she said, "I've made up my mind to get married. What I meant was, can you fix it so in case the son of a bitch and I don't get along, that he can't get any of my property?"

And he said, "Yes," says, "I can fix that part all right."

So she got married and a few years later I met her husband, a plumber, and when he found I was from Corsicana he says, "Do you know my wife?"

And I says, "Who was you wife?"

He says, "[Edith Block]."

I says, "Yes, I know of her."

"Well," he says, "you know people talk about me marrying a whore." Says, "I think it's something to be proud of." He said, "Any man can go out with a girl that's never been married and never had a sweetheart and persuade her to marry him, but," he says, "you take a man that takes a girl that has had ten thousand sweethearts and gets her to pick him out of all the rest and marry him," says, "now that's really doing something."

—Carl F. Mirus

OIL-

FIELD

CHARACTERS

7

It has been said that the oil industry attracted all kinds of people
from everywhere. In a sense this is true. Educational achievements
of those attracted ranged from functional illiterates to college and
professional-school graduates. Occupations represented included almost as many as are listed by the Census Bureau: lawyers, doctors,
actors, merchants, drug clerks, sawmill hands, farm boys. Yet they
had in common a venturesome spirit and a tendency toward non-
conformity. Ruth Sheldom Knowles calls her book on wildcatters
The Greatest Gamblers. The risks were great; the rewards for the
lucky were equally great. Although he often lost, it was said that the
wildcatter couldn't quit. Claude Witherspoon said that he never

knew of a practical oilman going broke; yet many practical oilmen, including Witherspoon, often wondered where the money for the next venture was coming from.

The workers—the drillers, the toolies, the roughnecks, the roustabouts, the pipe liners—were necessarily wanderers, for it required many fewer men to maintain a field than to develop it. When the limits of a pool had been defined and the wells had been drilled, the storage erected, and the pipe lines laid, the men moved on to a new discovery. The work was hard, the hours long, but wages were relatively high. The Protestant ethic applied: A worker could be sober and save his money, and become, as not a few did, an operator and perhaps a millionaire. On the other hand, in the temporary community of the boom town there was no compulsion to give sanction to this ethic. The worker who wished to could scorn the virtues of Poor Richard without loss of caste, which depended upon his skill. He could relieve the tensions of hard and dangerous work by going on a spree.

As the industry matured the organization man took over. Management is now dominated by conservative businessmen, whose risks are carefully calculated; and drillers and roughnecks live in comfortable towns and suburbs and differ little from their neighbors.

Walter Sharp

Usually, Mr. Sharp carried in his pockets some little gadget with which to while away the time he might have to wait. For instance, I remember he had a watch with a glass back on it. There were grooves inside and a shot, and he would amuse himself shaking that watch and trying to get the shot into the hole, bringing it around the grooves. Or, if he had nothing else available, he would sit and flip a coin, playing crackaloo.

You flip a coin and let it fall to the floor to see if it will fall on a crack, and if there are two people playing, then the one whose nickel or dollar or whatever it is gets closest to the crack wins the money. But these were merely methods of exhausting surplus energy. He was a very energetic and successful businessman. There's one instance I might tell that would be worthwhile to the oil business.

You'll have to understand that oil contract forms were not produced in perfection all at one time. They represent a growth and a correction and amendment from time to time by reason of experiences. For instance, Sharp was drilling a wildcat well at Sour Lake in the early days—it must have been about 1907—and thought that he was going to bring in a well. He came to Beaumont and went to the Gulf Company to make a contract to sell his oil. They agreed on the price; the contract was written up; and Walter went back to Sour Lake to bring in his well. In a few days he brought in a well making perhaps ten thousand barrels a day. He phoned the Gulf Company and told them that the well was in and to have the line hooked up. They asked him how much it was making. He said, "About ten thousand barrels." They said, "We can't take but about three thousand barrels. That's all the capacity we have available in the line." "Well," he said, "that doesn't make any difference." I'm not quoting his exact language—for various reasons. He said, "You have signed the contract to buy the oil produced from this well at a certain price and I am producing it and I expect you to take it or not." Well, this led to rather extensive negotiations, and finally a settlement was arrived at, and from that day to this, every oil purchase contract has contained a provision limiting the obligation to take to a certain number of barrels, giving the purchaser the option to take the balance, or such part of it as it may elect. The oil purchase contract is an aggregation of provisions, the necessity for which has been shown by things that occurred in the conduct of the business. The history of the oil purchase contract would fill a fair-size volume.

Not long after this, Sharp became connected with the Texas Company through his control, I believe, of the Producer's Oil Company, and his story would go on from there.

—E. E. *Townes*

I learned a lot about people out there and it reminded me of another thing that Mr. Sharp had taught me—Mr. Walter Sharp. I was in his office one day visiting with him. I had been working for him on some lease matters. He said, "Walter, did you know that people are just as honest as you make them believe that you think they are?" He said, "People will do anything if they get the idea that you expect them to do it." Says, "They'll never lie to you, never double-cross you, never steal from you."

And I said, "Well, that's a-going a good long ways."

"Well," he said, "I'll demonstrate." And he walked to his front office window, and across the street there a little Dago boy selling newspapers, and he told his secretary, he said, "Go down there on the street and tell that Dago I'll buy ten papers from him if he'll bring them up to my office." Well, he went down, stopped the little boy and told him, and, of course, he just came in a long trot.

When he came in the office, Mr. Sharp took a twenty-dollar bill out of his pocket. He said, "Son, take this down to the bank. You know where the bank is, down here about a block and a half." And he said, "I want it in ten dollars in one-dollar bills and ten dollars in fifty-cent pieces. You go down there and get it changed and bring it back."

And the little Dago took out. Left the office and Mr. Sharp said, "Now, do you think he's coming back?"

I said, "I don't know."

He said, "Well, I never saw him before, but I know he's coming back, because I expect him to come back, and he knows I expect him to come back, and he'll be back."

Well, in running my levee camp, I'd learned a bit of that. I was the only man, only foreman, the levee company had that didn't carry a Winchester rifle in a scabbard strapped onto the sweat leather on his horse, a six-shooter strapped around him, and a big hickory stick. I didn't carry anything. And yet I'd move more cubic yards of dirt per unit of man and mule and had fewer mules hurt and tore up, less equipment than anybody that worked for the company, because, rather than have all this firearms and things, I set up an emergency medical tent, and if they'd fall out in a coon-can game—you know, a little crap shooting or something and razor each other up a little bit—I got to be pretty good at this first aid and things; I just doctored them up. If I loaned them a dollar, I didn't expect two dollars Saturday. I just got my dollar back, and it wasn't but a little while until I had a hundred-odd Negroes. If they got in jail, I'd go down and pay their fines, never charge them anything. Just take a wagon and usually have the wagon loaded in jail every weekend, too.

I think people will do today just about what you expect them to do. If you can make them feel like that you believe in them, and know they're gonna do it, they'll do it. And that was Sharp's theory in handling men and his philosophy. He'd trust anybody. Made lots of jawbone trades. And I don't think he ever got double-crossed.

Showing the kind of a sport Walter Sharp was, though, I think it might be interesting to tell this. We were in one of the cafés, the dirty spoons, down at Humble one day, and there was Mr. Sims and Jim Sharp and somebody else in the crowd. I think it was Howard Hughes. Mr. Hughes owned the first automobile that I ever saw in my life, incidentally. Drove it around Houston. And he, I think, was in the group. We had to fan the flies off with one hand and eat with the other. The only safe thing to eat was ham and eggs. You could watch them cut the ham and see them break the eggs. And you had a pretty near even break with the flies from the stove to your plate, you know. We were sitting there and eating ham and eggs, and Mr. Sharp said, "Well, there's no use sitting here and not having any fun." Said, "Give me a piece of that bread." Gave him a piece of bread and he took some of this salve, looked like axle grease and it wasn't nearly as good as our present-day oleo, even the cheaper grades, but he took a knife and spread it very carefully over it, and cut it into four even-sized pieces and then took a level spoon of sugar out of the sugar bowl and sprinkled it evenly over each of the four pieces, and he put one piece in front of Howard Hughes, one in front of Jim Sharp, one in front of Walter Sharp. He said, "Now, I'll bet you birds a hundred dollars apiece that there'll be more flies land on my bread before we get through eating than there is on yours, and you can keep your own count."

Mr. Sharp picked me out of two or three crews he had working and came over to me and said, "Walter, I want you to come into Houston on the night train tonight. Come up to my office in the morning. I've got something I want you to do." Well, I showed up in his office the next morning and he said, "I want you to go over to Liberty and lease some land."

Well, frankly, I'd never seen a lease. I didn't know that's the way you got the right to drill wells or anything else, and I very promptly and honestly told him so.

"Well," he said, "I didn't think you knew anything about it. Nobody else does." Said, "You know as much as the rest of them and I think you're smarter than most of them." Says, "I'll get you some blank forms." And he got some blank form leases off a pad, gave me some money, and said, "Now, just catch this afternoon's train and get on over to Liberty and start leasing land."

"Well," I said, "Mr. Sharp, what ought I to pay for it?"

"Oh," he says, "hell, if I knew that, there wouldn't be much need in sending you. I'm sending you over there to pay whatever it takes. I want in. They're making a play over there, Barnsdall and Guffey and a bunch of them, and I don't know what there is to it, but I want to buy some leases, just over there whatever the rest of them are leasing."

—*Walter Cline*

Howard Hughes, Sr.

Howard Hughes came here as a young man and drilled a well at Sour Lake. He had a little money, but before completing his well he ran a little short, and Mr. Sharp let him have five hundred barrels of oil to fire his boiler and took a diamond stud as collateral. Then I had a cousin, Homer Chambers, who was superintendent and manager of the Gilbert Company at that time at Sour Lake, and he let him have five hundred barrels and took his watch as collateral. But Mr. Hughes was successful, and completed a good well, and paid both these debts back and redeemed his personal belongings.

I met him across the street here in front of the Texas Company Building at Pearl and Bowie one morning. There was a bunch of us boys looking at his automobile, and he had a Winton. I remember it had carbide lights and a lot of brass on it, and it had a cloth top; had a little tonneau in the back with a door and with seats facing one another so two people could sit in the back. And he said, "Boys, I got to go up to the Texas Company office here. You look at the car as long as you want to, but don't touch this brass; I worked on it all day yesterday."

He was a very energetic young man and really applied himself and was successful in the oil business. He developed one of the greatest rock bits in the world, the Hughes rock bit, which is still in use, and I'd say the leading rock bit of the world up to now.

—*W. C. Gilbert*

I believe in Sour Lake is the first time that I knew Mr. Hughes very well. And I didn't know him too well then. Mr. Hughes was a man that was a little hard to get acquainted with, especially a working man that wasn't in contact with him quite often. But I knew him, and he was generally with the Sharps or Colonel Crawford or those. And I did work for the Crawfords, and Mr. Hughes was possibly interested in work that I was doing, but I didn't know him from that angle. But Mr. Hughes was quite a character. He was a nice man to know, a nice man to be with. And he was energetic and full of theories and ideas.

We were going out to Pierce Junction in an old hack back in the early days before Pierce Junction was developed, and in the hack was Colonel Crawford, B. J. Harper, and Howard Hughes. There was some other man and myself. Well, all of these people generally had ten or fifteen silver dollars in their pockets and, while it was heavy, it was the money of the day. And Howard Hughes and the one that was on the back seat was flipping dollars or matching dollars, and it seemed like when we was coming back that we got along about where the old folks' home is there on Medina Road now. And there was an old darky walking alongside the road, and Howard told the driver, he says, "Stop this hack." And he called the old darky over, and they just dumped all those silver dollars right over in the old man's hat, pretty near filled his hat with silver dollars. Then he told the driver to drive on.

—*Curt G. Hamill*

The story goes that in the early days of the oil development either in Sour Lake, Batson, or Saratoga that Jimmy Sharp and a bunch were at a bar having a drink, and Howard drove up in a new automobile he had just purchased, and came in with his duster, and his goggles, and his cap on, and Jimmy looked him over with a lot of disgust. Jimmy said, "Bartender, do you have a check?" He said, "Yes." He said, "Give me one." So the bartender gave Jimmy a check, and Jimmy hollered down to the end of the bar, "Howard, how much did you pay for that automobile you are driving?" Howard told him thirty-five hundred or three thousand dollars, whatever it was, and Jimmy wrote out a check for cash and said, "Howard, I'll match you for the automobile and let the bartender pitch the dollar." Jimmy won the car. He said, "Any of you roughnecks or drillers know how to run an automobile?" They said, "No, we can run a drilling rig, but —maybe we can." So Jimmy said, "Howard, the duster, the cap, and everything goes with it." So they dressed one of these birds up in Howard's regalia, and they took a joy ride around for a while, and it was a couple of weeks before Howard got the automobile back.

—Charlie Lane

Governor Hogg in the Oil Field

Any history of Beaumont or Spindletop would not be complete without reference to that great and noble Texan, Governor James Stephen Hogg. Hogg, Judge Brooks, and others organized the Texas Company. Hogg was a very large man. One evening he was sitting in the lobby of the Crosby Hotel at Beaumont when I passed, and he asked me to stop and visit with him. Our conversation dealt with Spindletop. John W. Gates had just acquired a substantial interest in the stock of the Texas Company, and Hogg was disturbed, and his mental attitude doubtless led him to make a statement which I shall never forget. Quote: "The Texas Company is beginning to smell like Standard Oil, and I'm going to get out of it at the first favorable opportunity." But later, Judge Jim Robinson, of the law firm of Hogg and Robinson of Austin, was the prosecuting attorney in several cases wherein the state of Texas fined various oil companies several million dollars, and ousted them from Texas. All of these companies were alleged to belong to or [to be] subsidiaries of the Standard.

—H. P. Nichols

I recall meeting Judge Brooks when I first went to Beaumont and Spindletop. He and Governor Hogg and Jim Swayne, they had rented an office behind the bank at Beaumont, next to the Crosby House, the hotel there. This barbershop proprietor had a lease of twenty-five dollars a month, as I understood it. Brooks and Associates give him ten thousand dollars for his lease, to use that office.

I remember standing in the office there one day, and hearing Judge Brooks and Governor Hogg talking. Oil had been so plentiful, the price had dropped down to three cents. A lot of people made contracts for three cents a barrel for this oil, and those contracts were later knocked out by the court. But along about that time was when I heard them talking.

Governor Hogg was a fine gentleman, a fine man, and believed in Texas and Texas people. And he told Judge Brooks in this conversation, he said, "Ed, you know, I believe I'll have the legislature pass a law, that the people of Texas will never have to pay over twenty cents a barrel for oil produced in their state here."

And Judge Brooks said, "Well, hold on here, Governor. We're in the oil business. We don't care how high the oil goes."

—*Early C. Deane*

Governor Hogg was a very lovable character, and he at one time offered me all of Sour Lake. And he said, "I might put some money in with you if you'll go down there and drill us a well." But I didn't go because I didn't have the money to get off, and I didn't want to wildcat any more when the Spindletop had more oil than we could use. And at that time oil was worth, oh, eight and ten and fifteen cents a barrel.

I went to the Governor one time [later], and I got it in my head I'd like to drill a well for myself, and I went in and talked to him about it, and he always called me Curt. And I says, "Governor, I'd like to buy one of those little strips you got out there, those spots."

And he says, "Why, you don't want to produce oil." He says, "You can't sell the oil when you get it." And says, "You don't want to produce oil."

And I says, "Yes, I'd like to have a well of my own."

"Well," he says, "I'll sell you one of those blocks out there all right for—" a certain amount of money.

"Well," I says, "Governor, that sounds kinda high to me."

Well, he kinda reared back in his chair—he was a large man—and he says, "Well," he says, "Curt, Hogg's my name, and hog's my nature," and give a big hearty laugh. So, of course, I didn't buy the piece of ground.

—*Curt G. Hamill*

I used to see Governor Hogg at Sour Lake and then in Beaumont. And I can remember most vividly one time he lived at the Oaks Hotel when in Beaumont. Oaks Hotel was a wood-frame building, two or three stories high, out on Calder Avenue, quite a ways out from the business district. But because of poor drainage, we had lots of floods in Beaumont. You'd have a few flash thundershowers and you'd have a regular lake all over Beaumont. The surface drainage was insufficient to carry the water away rapidly enough. So one day, one hot morning, right after one of those flash floods, Governor Hogg wanted to come to the Texas Company's office, then in the Temperance Building down on Pearl Street. For some important reason he was coming down there. So he hired a skiff and a nigger that pulled it, a regular flatbottom, just an old flat-bottomed skiff. He was a huge man, he weighed about three hundred pounds, he was an awfully big man. He put a great big rocking chair in the middle of that skiff and he pulled his trousers up over his knees. And he had one of these great big umbrellas that you used to see on vegetable wagons. And it was made of red and white. And he was sitting in the rocking chair holding his umbrella to keep the sun off, it was awfully hot. And this nigger was pulling, pulling this flat-bottomed skiff down Calder Avenue. Well, everybody stopped, they were walking on sidewalks in water, everybody was walking, you know, in water. But they'd turn around and look at the skiff coming down the middle of Pearl. That was the only traffic on the street. Well, where the railroad crosses Pearl Street, the railroad is a little above the water, the Southern Pacific Railroad. He came up to there and it took him about half an hour, I guess, to get out of that skiff and the nigger to snake it across the rails and into the water again on the other side of the railroad track. And he got back in there in the rocking chair, and the nigger pulled him on down to the stairs to go upstairs in the Temperance Hall. And he got out and went on in the office there.

—*Burt E. Hull*

Ed Sims

Ed Sims was a bit different. He owned a bluegrass farm in Kentucky and raised race horses; and I worked for him on a well out there that blew out. And it really blew out. It was out on the north side of the field, the old Mason lease, drilled in a cornfield. And the well started blowing out and my derrick man hooked a leg and an arm over his emergency escape line. Because, if you don't know, in those days, not having any other safety devices, we improvised one which was a part of a cathead line and tied in a V of the derrick right back of where the derrick man worked and then slanted off into the woods, tied to a tree or a stump or a log somewhere sixty or seventy yards away from the rig. And when trouble started on the derrick floor, as it frequently did in those days, why, the derrick man was in a good deal of danger. If a fire started, he burned and fell just like a crippled squirrel. I've seen a dozen of them burn up in the derrick. And rock could hit him; pipe could hit him and kill him. He was the most vulnerable man you had, so we gave him this safety line. All he had to do was know that he was gonna burn the skin off of his inside of his elbow and the inside of his knee sliding down this grass rope at about a mile a minute, but that's better than getting hit and knocked out.

So the derrick man slid down and the rest of us vacated. I cut out firing the boilers and shut my machinery down and we all started running. Ran out in this cornfield and the four-inch drill pipe we had was being fed out through the top of the derrick, the top of the derrick by that time having been knocked off. It was just two sides of the derrick wobbling around, and occasionally one of them would peel off. This four-inch pipe would feed up in the air some four or five or six joints and then break off just like macaroni, and pitch over and stick up in the field or in the woods somewhere.

After it got through that, it kept blowing a bigger hole and finally started caving in and shutting itself off. And then it would build up a heavy gas and blow through again and we'd see parts of our machinery and part of the derrick timbers flipped up. The boilers finally went in and the pipe in front of the V went in and we got over on an old leaning tree, where we could watch it perform, and saw that a neighboring farmer over there with a dug well that had developed all of a sudden a gas well that was spewing enough to run all of his stock out of the pen, the way he had them penned up. They just broke through a flimsy-looking wooden gate and went out to the big pasture.

Following this blowout, I realized that we had lost a complete rig and all of the drill pipe, boilers included, and derrick, and fully expected to be fired. Mr. Sims and some of his associates on the well, he heard about it and came out on the train and got his buckboard and team of ponies from the livery stable and drove out and found us sitting on this log and the well was still acting up a little bit. Came over and sat down and he said, "Who was on duty when this happened?"

And I says, "I was. I'm the driller."

"Well," he said, "son, let me congratulate you."

"Well," I said, "now, Mr. Sims, I know I'm going to get fired. I don't mind being paid off, but I don't like to be kidded. I'd rather have my check and not any conversation."

"Oh," he said, "I have no intention of firing you." He says, "You did a fine thing for me." He said, "What I need is a little more publicity." And he said, "Now, if you'd a had a little old dinky two-by-four blowout and just got my pipe stuck, I'd fired you. But if you have a blowout and have the biggest one that's ever been in Texas, my God, that's something to brag about. And I'm proud of you." Said, "I'm not kidding." He said, "Come, get in the buckboard. We'll drive uptown and buy you a new rig."

—*Walter Cline*

Mr. Sims was a fine-looking man and a very pampered man. The first time I saw him he came to Goose Creek and he had one man carrying his overcoat, another man carrying his raincoat, and a third man carrying a box of cigars, and a fourth man carrying a briefcase, which I assumed had a bottle of whiskey in it. A regular retinue. He enjoyed that. He liked to put on a good show.

Same way in later years at New Orleans when he went to a restaurant there. He always managed to be the center of attraction. Throw dishes on the floor or holler across the room at the headwaiter that something wasn't cooked properly, or, I remember one night in Antoine's, he ordered their pompano *en papillote*. When the waiter got the sack opened, turned it on his plate, he asked for some Tabasco sauce. The waiter threw up his hands in horror and told him that it was well seasoned in the kitchen. Mr. Sims insisted he wanted Tabasco sauce, so the headwaiter came. Finally Roy Alcaitore, the proprietor, came up. He told Mr. Sims that this dish was seasoned fit for the gods in the kitchen and any addition to it would be a desecration. The old man looked at it and says, "Listen here," says, "I don't give a goddam if this dish suits you or it suits the waiter or it suits your goddam cook," he says, "I'm the man paying for it." Says, "I want some Tabasco sauce." So they brought it.

—*Carl F. Mirus*

Judge Pintelle

Just trying to think of that little old town over there at Louisiana. Howard I. Vincent is the head, is the whole town, pretty nearly. He's a big rancher and, well, I had quite an experience there. I didn't, couldn't talk that language. Cajun French. I couldn't talk it and I couldn't drink that coffee, neither, so I got a fellow to go with me, a halfbreed over there.

There's an old fellow by the name of Judge Pintelle. Judge Pintelle had red whiskers come down to here, and he had a little old pine hut there but he had a sweet-gum tree, the largest I ever saw, right out in his yard. He sat out under it, moss hanging down pretty near to the ground, you know. They said if I could get Pintelle to sign, well, I wouldn't have any trouble then. So I went in there and talked to the judge. Now he says, "No, Mr. Witherspoon, I wouldn't let you come in here and drill a well at all." Said, "I know you'd get a hundred-thousand-barrel well," and said, "I got a nice place here." Just a frog pond, you know, was all it was. "And I wouldn't have this place ruined with that old stinking oil at all." Beaumont oil, he called it. And I couldn't talk to him. Just wouldn't talk about it at all. And I got this fellow that was helping me and he went by there and the old judge just wouldn't have anything to do with an oilman at all.

We went in there, and I guess I leased eight or ten thousand acres of land. Old Colonel Stribling was going to drill a well. He did. He drilled a well in close there. He drilled on Howard I. Vincent's place, and every day, it just got to be funny, every time I'd start out in that direction I'd go by and talk to old Pintelle, just to see what he'd say, you know. Make out like I thought he'd changed his mind, you know, hoped he had, and I made a practice of it. I guess I went to see that old fellow a dozen times. Always be sitting under that sweet-gum tree. So I got ready to leave. I had an inkling that by some ruse that maybe I could get that lease. Well was drilling not very far from it, and so I drove up to the gate and got out and went in. Judge was glad to see me. We'd gotten pretty well acquainted, you know.

So I said, "Well, Judge, I'm getting ready to go home. Going to leave on this next train. And I've certainly enjoyed meeting you and your wife and just wanted to come by and tell you good-by and enjoyed my visit here with you. Very nice." Whole lot of stuff like that. He said, "Well," says, "I certainly have enjoyed talking to you." Said, "You seem to be fair about everything."

I said, "I guess you haven't changed your mind about giving me a lease, giving me a permit, right to come in and drill a well on this thing."

"Well," he said, "I been thinking about that thing, and, of

course, I don't want any oil well here on my place. I wouldn't live here at all." Then he says, "If I could live, didn't live here, if I got that well I'd leave. I'd want to sell this place."

And I said, "Well, Judge, what'd you take for this place?" He said, "Well, if I can get a hundred-thousand-barrel oil well here on it, why, I don't know." Finally he said he'd take a hundred dollars an acre for it.

I said, "Well, Judge, I'll tell you what I'll do. I'll show you that my heart's in the right place. If you give me the right to come in here and drill a well anywhere I want to within three years of that time, take or leave, I'll agree that if I come in here and drill and get a well that makes a hundred thousand barrels of oil a day"—that's all he could talk was a hundred thousand barrels—"hundred thousand barrels of oil a day for thirty consecutive days, I'll give you two hundred dollars an acre."

Said, "Sounds more like it." Said, "I always thought you were a fair man." Says, "Mary, come out here."

His wife come out and she said, "Now, Tom, I told you all the time Mr. Witherspoon was a fair man. I told you all the time."

And they signed it and I put it on record at Lake Charles, leased it for three years with an absolute stipulation that I was to pay them two hundred dollars an acre in cash whenever that well on that place made as much as one hundred thousand barrels a day for thirty consecutive days. The oil would have been four feet deep. That's the way I got that lease. It's on record over there now. Drilled and got a dry hole. That was all there was to it.

—*Claude Witherspoon*

Breck Walker

Breck Walker, in spite of the wealth that he acquired, he was really a very human sort of a guy. I had our money in one of the state banks, or in his bank to start with up at Breckenridge, back when all the banks were going broke there in the early '20s. And I had heard so many things about the First National Bank going broke, I told my wife, "By George, we've heard so much of that, let's take our money out of there and take it up to this other state bank."

So we drug her out and took it up to the state bank. By golly, two or three days later the darn state bank went busted. And the next morning after that, it'd got every crying nickel we had. We had taken it out of Breck's bank. And I come down along past the First National, and here was Breck standing out one sunny morning, standing out on the steps. And he said, "Well, Ed, I guess you're glad this morning that you're doing business with us."

I said, "Breck, there's where the joke is. I heard you birds was going broke and I took my money out of here day before yesterday, and took it up to that outfit that went broke yesterday."

"Well, now," Breck said, "that's just too bad. You need any money?"

And I said, "Well, I could use some."

"Well," he said, "you go in and I'll okay a check for you here for a hundred dollars. Now you pass this around to any of the working boys, the boys that is working. They're probably in a pinch on account of that bank up there. Come down and I'll honor their check for a hundred dollars. I don't want these stewbums, but your people that you know that are working here, tell them to come down and I'll honor their check for a hundred dollars."

Well, now, you know, that's pretty good. He wasn't doing it for any political or any financial gain or anything. He had it, and he made it all at Breckenridge. He leased some of the best part of the Breckenridge field, ten cents an acre, while he was still mail carrier, carried the route from Ranger to Breckenridge. Well, he took up some of the early leasing around there. When the T. P. Coleman Oil was leasing some of their first in there, old Breck, he gets in, he shoves in a few nickels. And he got the best part of the field there, but at ten cents an acre, with a yearly rental of another dime, great big round dime. And then he'd put that out to the promoters that wanted to drill there, for not an eighth overright but one half, laid on top of the ground for him.

Well, it was right in proven territory, and it was a good deal all the way around. But that's where Breck got his money—and oil three-fifty a barrel, when most of it was drilled up. The flush production off of Waler holdings went into the pipe lines at three-fifty a barrel, and of course, not long after that, in '21 or '22, they soon knocked down to around ninety cents, but most of the flush production of that Breckenridge territory was three-fifty oil, before the so-called panic or whatever you want to call it that happened in late '21 and '22.

—E. P. Matteson

Cheeky Morgan

There was Cheeky Morgan. Cheeky was supposed to have been the fastest promoter that ever hit the oil country. Cheeky was a nickname. Cheeky, and that's how he got it, I suppose, because he had the cheek to do about anything. One of his stunts they tell on him, that along the Ohio River, between Ohio and West Virginia, Cheeky Morgan stole a string of pipe one time, and moved it across the Ohio River and run it into his well. During the legal procedure that took place, it took so darn long going from one state to another that the well came in and he was a great fellow and paid off.

—*E. P. Matteson*

Bad Check

And there used to be quite a number of characters, especially among the contractors. They had one fellow, they called him Bad Check, and he's got a lot of relatives in the oil country, and if everybody that ever reads this knows who we're talking about, it's because for thirty years he was known as Bad Check. I worked for him, and I got all the money that I ever had coming, and I can't complain. But he wasn't the easiest guy to work in the world, to get money out of.

They tell one on Bad Check: One day he was walking down the street by himself, and he was so darn used to a fellow running after him trying to collect some money for back wages and so forth that out of the corner of his eye—it was a sunny day—he saw his shadow walking along beside him and he said, "Pay you tomorrow. Yes, pay you tomorrow." That was just right on the end of his tongue. He was always ready to put them off till tomorrow.

He never did come into money. By golly, I'll tell you what. This same guy really got in the money, but went to a hospital in California and was operated on and died, by golly, before he knew what he had done. His heirs got the money, and he just hard-lucked it all the way through. Well, funny deal.

—*E. P. Matteson*

Pete Hoffman

One of the old-time oilmen that I would like to talk about more than anyone else is a man they called Pete Hoffman. He was a generation ahead me in age, and he had started out in Pennyslvania and drifted down as the boom subsided. He had drifted down to my native state of West Virginia and operated for a good many years, and then come West with the other oilmen who left the town for other states like Illinois, Oklahoma, Kansas, and on down to Texas. He died here in Cisco six or seven years ago.

He is one of the most noted characters, and one man that I always said never had the slightest thought or care of what anyone else thought about him—didn't care what his neighbors might say of what he did. He was of a very big build, enormous physical strength, and if he wanted anything off the neighboring wells, he would take it and carry it over the hills and bury it. When he thought that they would not think of it any more, he would dig it up and use it. I can remember in West Virginia being out with some oilmen maybe where there was some fresh mound of dirt, possibly where some farmer had buried a farm animal, and one of the men would kick it with his foot as he went by and say, "Well, there is where Pete buried a set of jars or a rope socket," or something like that.

So he is supposed to be the one that had stolen the boiler with the steam in it that he used. That story has been told of many others, but he is really supposed to be the one who did it first. They were using the boiler and all the men went to dinner. He had his team ready, and he disconnected the lines from the boiler and with the steam mains on the boiler, he hoisted it to his team and hauled it away. When the men came back from dinner the boiler was gone. I suppose they found it later. This boiler was mounted on wheels like they sometimes did these smaller boilers. I suppose they called it a twenty-horsepower boiler. I imagine it took four or six horses possibly to haul it over West Virginia hills. Had the water and the steam in it that they been using.

I never knew him getting into serious trouble. I never heard him serving a penitentiary sentence. I know he always paid for the material that he had taken if he was cornered—cornered enough where he would have to. It has been more or less a sort of a custom—oil-country custom—when you wanted a tool, to go to the neighboring rig and borrow it. If they were not working at the rig, shut out, possibly finished a well and the tools were just lying there idle, just go out there and get it. So it is pretty hard to tell when stealing started in and borrowing quit.

Pete Hoffman was a right successful operator and died a few years ago supposedly worth a quarter of a million dollars in cash, and his money was located in many different banks, so that if one bank failed, it wouldn't hurt him any. He had it stacked away in many banks in Texas, Louisiana, or so the story goes. He disposed of most of his properties.

One story we have of Pete Hoffman which is true—an old oil-country story. He was operating out of a town of West Virginia, called Clarksburg, which was centrally located, and at that time a streetcar line and railroads ran out from the town in many directions. So the story goes that Pete got a woman and they, together in partnership, started an immoral resort in the town of Clarksburg, close to the depot in a section of Clarksburg which has always been known as Glendale.

That section of Clarksburg has always had a bad name; even yet today that name would be a handicap to that part of town. So the story goes that Pete had his office in this resort and he would send his four men to drill a well maybe out ten miles, maybe twenty miles, and they would be gone for forty days, probably fifty, in extreme cases. Then when they came back into his office, he would pay them off. Then the landlady would cash their checks. Then, of course, the girls would get at them to buy the drinks and some of the younger single men would never get away from there, and in four, five days, a week, their money would be gone, so Pete then would start them out again, maybe in a different direction. And then in another month or month and a half, the same performance would be repeated. The men didn't like it a bit. It kind of got the men to talking among themselves.

The story goes that the men were drinking—Clarksburg was then a saloon town—the men were drinking over Saturday night so they decided to put Pete out of business. And on the lawn of the depot they had a Spanish War cannon. So they got powder and they crammed it down this cannon, they filled it full of railroad spikes, bolts, and pieces of iron and rocks, and aimed it just on top of this hill where they could see the top of Pete's house—just the upper part of his house—so they aimed and touched off this cannon, and they just swept the top of his house off just like a cyclone. The men said they got too much powder in the cannon. The cannon jumped up and down and turned over a few times and went on its back on the lawn. I heard different people say that they heard the report all over Clarksburg and it just jarred as if some enormous explosion— and no one knew what had happened, except those that were in the know about it.

Out came Pete to see what had happened. He knew that something was wrong with his house as it shook from one end to the other. So out followed the men that were there for the night— the girls that stayed there for their home. So they got to going over the damage, and Pete discovered that the top of his house was gone. At this time, of course, he didn't know what had happened, but he did know that he was out of part of his house—all swept off. The next day he started to put two and two together, and got some information here and there. So some of the fellows that were in the deal had to leave town.

This is an old oil-country story, and some of the older oilmen will talk of that yet. Another thing in connection with Pete Hoffman I have always thought of and often remarked on—I have never heard his name mentioned to one of the older oilmen that he didn't break out in a laugh. You just mention his name yet—Pete Hoffman—to some old-time oilman and you will see him start laughing.

—*O. G. Lawson*

Something happened in our Sistersville, West Virginia, store one time. This may seem rather funny, but it's an actual fact. We at that time were selling a lot of boilers. We lost one. We knew that somebody got it, that we either failed to make a charge for it or somebody hauled it out of the yards without our knowing anything about it. We couldn't check it up; we couldn't find it. We looked over a period of time for it, and finally decided the only way to find out if some of our customers did get that boiler was to make a charge to every one of them. We made a charge to all of our customers that we'd been selling boilers to over a period of years. When the time came, we got those letters all mailed, bills all made out. First of the month we got a check from Mr. Pete Hoffman for that boiler. Now we don't know to this day whether he got it or not, but anyway he paid for it.

—*Carl Angstadt*

Well, at one time he stole a set of jars, and that's one they tell on him, of course. And Pete stole a set of jars from another guy and packed them on his back about a half a mile after night. He threw them down over his rig and the guy looked down and seen that there was a crack in the jars, that they were broken. Old Pete says, "Some of these damn guys are going to get in bad, running that kind of junk." That's one they tell on him.

—*E. P. Matteson*

I heard one story about old Pete. Stole an eight-inch cable-tool bit. And there's not a man can carry one of those, you know. And evidence showed that he never did drive in to the rig. He stopped his wagon out in the road, you know, and walked out to the rig and carried that bit out there and put it in that wagon, you know.

That's what the evidence showed that he did. Never did show that he ever went to the rig with a wagon to haul it, you know. And they had this bit in the courthouse laying there. And the jury was there and this bit. Man stole this bit and carried it from that rig out to the wagon over there? And they knew there ain't no one man could carry that bit. And he just couldn't carry it, it was just too big. So when they freed him, you know, cleared him, he wasn't guilty of stealing that bit at all. And when they got through, to the judge he said, "This my bit, now?" "Yes, sir." He just got it in his arms and went on out. Picked it right up.

—*H. A. Rathke*

Toledo Jack

Old Toledo Jack was the guy that was always mooching everybody. He was a driller, but he'd gotten on to the rum so much that he was just about worthless. But he was like a lot of those stewbums that if you could keep him working, he was a darn good, a pretty good boy. But there at Breckenridge some guy come in and got him to go out four or five days extra, and he had to have a man. And I think it was twenty dollars a day. When he came back he gave him a check for eighty dollars. He went in the bank and got it all in one-dollar bills.

And this actually happened. He stood right on the steps of the

First National Bank up there and every man, woman, and child that come along, he give them one dollar. Give her all away. Said, "I'll show the people of this town that I'm no damn piker. They've kept me for three or four years, and I'll just give it back to them."

—E. P. Matteson

Dad Titus

During my days on the Rio Grande border, east of Loredo, while we were developing this little gas field, we frequently used the combination rig, setting pipe near the gas pay with the rotary and then drilling it in with a cable tool. I had among our employees at that time a man named Titus. He was a descendant of the original Titus for whom Titusville, Pennsylvania, is named, and it being one of the pioneer communities in the development of the oil industry made Dad Titus a very colorful and a very interesting character to have at camp. Possibly the most pronounced eccentricity he had was the habit of wanting to work the graveyard shift. That is, working from twelve o'clock at night until twelve o'clock noon. And he wouldn't work the afternoon shift, though he had the experience and the priority and the right to that tower if he wanted it.

Our boardinghouse keeper was an excellent cook, and she used to prepare a very wholesome and bounteous meal for the men who went out at midnight to eat between eleven and eleven-thirty, and then packed their breakfast baskets for them so they'd have something out of their lunch pail for breakfast at seven o'clock the next morning.

Well, Mr. Titus was a pretty fair, two-fisted eater, and I'd usually push tools between midnight and seven o'clock in the morning. I didn't care very much to drive by one of my rigs at ten o'clock in the forenoon or four o'clock in the afternoon, it being reasonable to assume that everybody would be on their toes and fighting the bottom of the hole at those hours, but it is interesting sometimes if you want to make a little money in the contracting business to drop around between twelve o'clock and seven A.M.

So frequently I'd saddle up my little broomtail pony and ride around to the rigs and on two or three occasions I had noticed that when Dad Titus would come out with his lunch pail and go into the toolroom close to the band wheel on his standard-cable tool rig, change his clothes, come out and get on his work stool, before he started letting out any screw or trying to make any hole, he'd get his lunch pail, put it in between his knees, look into the top layer, then lift that out and look under the bottom, and if there was an orange in there, he laid it out. And if there was a banana or an apple, he'd put it out; a piece of pie, he'd lay it out. Cake, he'd put that out. Or a particular tasty salad or something, he'd put it out.

Well, I'd sit in the brush sometimes and watch him, and sometimes I'd walk up on the derrick floor. The procedure was always the same and unvarying. So about the third or fourth time I'd dropped by his rig just as he went on tower, I asked him, I said, "Dad, what the Sam Hill is the big idea of eating all you want up there at the boardinghouse, which is a delicious and wholesome and well-cooked meal, and then bringing a well-packed pail out here for your breakfast and sitting down before you ever hit a lick of work and picking out everything that's tasty and good in it and eating it?"

The old man looked at me and smiled a kind of a dry smile and his eyes twinkled and he says, "You know, son, I'm a good deal older than you are, and I've been around drilling rigs longer than you have. You'd be surprised how many things can happen to your lunch." He says, "You know, the rig can burn down, you don't have anything to eat. The ants can get in it." He said, "It can fall off the nail and a stray dog, the hogs around, they . . ." Said, "There's so many different things that can happen to it, that I've made up my mind, and have been practicing it for years and it works out all right." Said, "Even though I eat a good meal up at the boardinghouse, when I get out to the rig, I look through my pail and see what there is that I know I'd like to have if I could save it until breakfasttime the next morning, but I just can't afford to take the chance and I eat it right then."

And another one of his interesting remarks that he made to me—and this is strictly from a family man's viewpoint—at the time he was working for me, our first two babies had come along, a boy and a girl. And, of course, I was very proud of them and was bragging to Dad Titus about it and he said, "Well, that's a nice family, Walter, and raising a boy and a girl with the present expense is a pretty big load." He said, "I expect you'd better slow down now and stop your production for a while till you see how you get along. You're still working for a salary."

I said, "No. I tell you what my wife and myself made up our mind to. I ordered a boy and—the first time—and he came as per my order. Then my wife wanted a girl and, of course, I stood aside and let her have her way and the girl came along. And now I want another boy. I'd like to have two boys, so we're—we're going to go ahead and have another boy, and then slow up."

The old man looked at me with a twinkle in his eye and he said, "Now, son, I keep reminding you that I'm older than you are, and I've seen more living than you have." He said, "You and your wife are kind of set on another boy?"

I said, "Oh, hell, yes. We've definitely made up our mind to it. We're going to have another boy."

"Well," he said, "you're both young and that's all right if that's what you got your mind made up to, but I'll tell you, and you might remember this. That's a hell of a good way to raise a big family."

—*Walter Cline*

Grant Emory

Well, we had so many eccentric characters that it would be hard to know which one to single out. We had one that we like to talk about, called Grant Emory. He died in recent years in Fort Worth, and for many years, he had said that his age was seventy-nine—never got past that—but supposedly his age was up in the eighties. He had been a hard drinker for a man with better than average education at that time. I have always heard that he had been educated for a priest, but drinking got the best of him, and he finally ended up as a perfect sot, and in later years when I knew him he was a generation ahead of me in age. He would work around erratically sometimes for as long as a month and then he would go spend the money for whiskey, and he would be drunk as long as he had any money or as long as he could borrow some, but I happen to remember that he always used tomatoes to sober up on. He would go to the grocery store, buy tomatoes by the can, and drink the juice.

He was of a sarcastic, cynical turn and uncommunicative. I heard one story about him. He had gone to work with a new tool dresser at twelve o'clock noon one day and the tool dresser knew of him. He wouldn't speak to Grant and Grant wouldn't speak to him so that both worked to along till about seven that night without either one speaking to the other. Each one was an old hand at the business and knew what to do without having to give orders or talk it over with each other. So the story goes that the tool dresser had come in from the boiler and had seen to the west a storm coming up, lightning and thundering, so he said, "Well, Mr. Emory, looks as if we will have to go home in the rain tonight." Mr. Emory said, "Young man, you talk too much."

—O. G. Lawson

One time Emory was in the boardinghouse, boarding at Ranger, at one of these old family tables, old-time tables—serve old-time meals, just set all the stuff on the table, sit down there and start eating. And they had hot biscuits one morning and Mr. Emory was using a lot of butter, and the landlady noticed it and said, "Mr. Emory, you know that butter is costing me seventy-five cents a pound?"

Emory stuck his knife in the butter and got another big hunk of it and slapped it on the biscuit and said, "It's worth every damn cent of it."

—Carl Angstadt

I dressed tools for Grant Emory. Oh, a long time ago, and two or three different occasions. Jim Dunagan up here at Breckenridge, of the Dunagan Tool Supply, I heard him tell about one time that Toledo Jack and Yeller Young came down to the shop down there, to his machine shop, and come in with a very sad story—collecting money to bury old Grant.

He said, "Grant died last night, you heard about it?"

"No," Jim says, "I haven't heard it."

"Yes, they found him dead up there in bed. Well, we're around taking up a little money. If you'd like to kick in a little something we'd appreciate it, Jimmy."

And so Jimmy said he give them twenty dollars. Went uptown after while—oh, four or five hours later—and here come Yeller and Toledo Jack and old Grant, with their arms around one another singing and having a big time. God, that's the way they went around and mooched, boy. They had an idea, to have old Grant dead, and nearly everybody would kick in a little money, you know.

Close to a year later they forgot who they'd mooched the time before, see. So they had Grant die again. They came in and told Jimmy, said, "You heard about Grant?"

"No, I haven't heard about him."

"Well, they found him dead in bed up here this morning. We're around taking up a little collection to bury the old boy."

And, Jim says, he'd remembered the first one. He said, "I went too strong on the first one, so I just kept my mouth shut and handed them ten. I cut it down. The boys had to have some fun, so I passed him ten dollars that time." Going to bury Grant again. That was one way of getting a few drinks.

—E. P. Matteson

Gib Morgan

I had a letter from the *Saturday Evening Post*. They wanted me to write them some stories on Gib Morgan, you know, the great Gib Morgan. Well, I knew him; I growed up, you know, I knowed his boys. And when I was up in Indiana he was in the soldiers' home there. Well, I'd always on a afternoon go out there, you know, and visit with him.

Well, there's a fellow name of Bridgeman and an old driller name of Leeper. They wanted to meet him. Well, I said, "All right, we'll just go out this afternoon." And he always sat right at the gate, you know, and there was a saloon right on the outside of the gate. Well, we went out there and I introduced him to these two fellows. So old Gib said to them, said, "Don't believe anything he tells you. 'Tain't true, you know." Of course, he'd knowed me ever since a kid.

So they took him out into the saloon and shot two or three drinks into him. Come back and sat down on this bench and while we were sitting there here come a fellow along on a bicycle. And Leeper said to him, "I believe I'd sooner have a pony than a bicycle."

Old Gib looked at him a little bit and he said, "You ought to see my bicycle."

Old Bill said, "What kind of a bicycle you got?"

Well, he says, "It's three hundred feet high and I can carry a good-sized trunk on it." Well, you know, I'd heard all these stories so much that I'd told 'em to different fellows, you know, and finally the *Saturday Evening Post* wrote me a letter and wanted me to write some of these stories for them.

—C. C. McClelland

I have heard Gib Morgan stories ever since I was a boy, and to give you a little idea of him, he was a Civil War veteran and when he come back from the war he started working in the oil fields in Pennsylvania, but drink soon got the better of him, and he eventually became an oil-country tramp. But he had a wonderful mind and would have been a wonderful novelist, I have always thought, if he would have had the education and training.

He had a wonderful imagination, and oilmen would go down to the supply store and get him drunk just to hear him tell stories. Most of his stories were more or less technical nature and it would hardly be interesting to those that did not understand the terms and the conditions that we worked under in the oil fields. But one story has come to mind that I like to laugh about myself as I am driving around in my work during the day.

The story goes that he was promoting a well at Allen, West Virginia. He was going to go into the oil business himself. He promoted this well and started drilling, and had bad luck and soon ran out of money, and he owed everybody in the country; he owed men for labor and everybody else that he could possibly owe in the country. He saw that he could never make a go of it, so he left one night. He said that fifty years later he was going through West Virginia, and he thought that the country looked familiar to him. He saw a drilling well just up against the hillside—so he thought he would just go up to that drilling well just to see who was there. So he said he walked in on the deck and here were the drilling crew and tool dressers with great long beards that reached down to their waists hopping around the decks with canes and the driller looked up at him and said, with an old, cracked voice, "Well, Gib, we thought you'd be back." They were fifty years drilling and waiting for Gib to come back to pay them. This is one of his many stories.

—*O. G. Lawson*

Sam Nepley

We used to have a character around here, Sam Nepley. He was quite a character, quite a witty character. I was sitting in the store one morning, and he came in—this was about the time that some of the banks were going broke. He came in and said, "Carl, you got any money in this bank around here?"

And I said, "Yeah, I have a little, Sam. Why?"

And he said, "Well, you better go get it out. I saw that cashier looking at a timetable while ago."

Another morning he came in, told me they had a new man around at the bank. I says, "Oh, I didn't know that."

He says, "Yeah, they got a new one around there."

And I says, "What's his name?"

He says, "I don't know. I don't know what his name is. All I know is that his initials are on the bank statement—'O. D.'"

This happened in Cushing, Oklahoma, way back in the old days when they were really tough back there. Bunch of pipe liners were in the store one day, talking, popping off, and pretty hard for the store manager to get his work done. And they started telling how many lines that they'd worked on all over the country, all over the United States, part of Mexico and different parts of the world, and the store manager finally got just a little bit tired of it. He raised up and looked over at 'em, and said, "I'll bet you I can tell you a line you fellows never worked on."

One old hophead says, "What line's that?"

He says, "It's the Mason and Dixon Line."

He says, "The devil we didn't! We carried water on it!"

—Carl Angstadt

Lew Teatra

And we had another character around here, Lew Teatra.

They'd congregate around the store; they'd tell stories; they'd drill wells in that store—and one morning they were talking about cyclones. Mr. Teatra sat there for a long time, never said a word, and they were telling about straws being blown through telephone poles and all the different capers that a cyclone would cause or do—you'd get a little bit tired of hearing it. And he said, "You know, I had an experience in a cyclone one time, up in Kansas."

He said, "A little town"—I did remember the name of the town; I can't recall it now—"had a big cyclone up there and it blew everything down in that town but the Catholic church. I went up to see it, and I's walking around through the debris there, looking around, and I heard a rooster crow. I looked around for that rooster and I couldn't see anything of him. Crowed a second time, and I looked around some more and I couldn't find him. I went home, went to bed, and I got to thinking of that rooster after I got in bed. I just couldn't figure out where he was. I got up early the next morning and went back up there. I got to walking around through that debris again, kicking things around, and I heard this rooster crow, though. I walked around a little more and I came to a two-gallon jug. I just gave that jug a little kick with my foot and that thing bursted open and out jumped that rooster, out of that jug."

The wind had blown him through the small neck of the jug. And that stopped the cyclone stories at that particular time!

—Carl Angstadt

Yorky

That was quite a character. I knew him very well. He came here during the boom. They say he was dressed up in Prince Albert; sixty thousand dollars in his pocket; but he liked to drink, and everything was wild in Beaumont then, and he stayed around the hotels and saloons in Beaumont, and, while he was a highly educated man, he done nothing. Just stayed there until he was broke. He was very proud. His folks had money. They was looking for him, trying to prevail upon him to come home, but he said he wouldn't go back unless he could go back like he left.

I remember one time he had a couple of letters. Said, "Keep them for me. I know what's in them." He said, "Checks, and I'm not going to use them. Gonna send them back." They wanted him to help settle an estate, and I think it was his sister that got in communication with a friend of mine and offered to pay his expenses and give him a thousand dollars if he could get him back to New York, but he never was able to do it. He disappeared. I don't know when he left or whatever happened to him.

He was a man that could answer any question you asked him, and one night I was sitting out in front of Walter Berry's store there, and somebody was playing the piano over there. He said, "I'd like to have ahold of that." I didn't know then that he was also an accomplished musician. He went over there and pounded the ivory over there. I would say he was in the early fifties, I believe. I know his real name, but perhaps I had better keep it off the record.

When I was supposed to go to Mexico and Yorky heard about it, and he says, "Before you go, you come see me. I'm going to give you a letter to the president of the First National Bank in Mexico City." He says, "You don't need to tell him who I am today or what

I am today." But he says, "He remembers me, a personal friend of mine. He'll be worth a lot to you." But I didn't go to Mexico; so I didn't get the letter.

—Harry R. Paramore

Lucky Hunter

Mr. Hal Greer was a lawyer here [at Beaumont], lived here the greater part of his life. And he was quite a deer hunter. So he went out close to where the Saratoga field is now located in Hardin County and he killed a big buck and hung him up to a tree limb there and dressed him. After he had completed this job there was a small pond there, and he noticed some bubbles on it, but didn't pay a great deal of attention to that. And he had his boots on, so he walked out in and washed up.

He said he always smoked cigars and always would take a match and light a piece of wax paper, so he could get a good blaze to light his cigar. And he said, "After I washed up—why, I was just standing there and I decided I'd light a cigar in the usual manner, of course. When I threw the wax paper down, the pond caught on fire, and I said, "Well, this is certainly a good oil showing; there's gas here."

And he says, "Before I broke camp and left, I purchased three acres of land from the farmer there."

When the Saratoga field came in along about 1904—why, a gentleman came to Mr. Greer and leased his land, but Mr. Greer put in there that he had to drill to a certain depth, around 1100 feet, as well as I remember. And the man drilled this well down to about 1085 feet and came in to report to Mr. Greer that he had fulfilled his contract and he hadn't discovered any oil. Mr. Greer says, "Well, how deep did you drill?"

Says, "1085."

"Well," he says, "my contract specifically says that you have to drill to a depth of 1100 feet. You'll have to go back and drill it fifteen feet deeper before I'll release it."

He went back and drilled the fifteen feet and got a good well. And Mr. Greer derived quite a royalty off this land during his lifetime, and I imagine his family now is getting a small royalty off of this three-acre tract.

—W. C. Gilbert

A Hot Runner

I was employed in a large number of what was called hot-oil cases. That's cases where the lease operator, the man who owned the lease and operated the well, would produce oil in excess of the allowable permitted by the Railroad Commission. And he would settle with the royalty owners and sometimes with his associates and the owners in the lease only for the legitimate oil. And he would pocket the rest. In fact, there was two prices in the oil field for oil, one for legitimate oil and another cheaper price for hot oil. When legitimate oil, that produced according to the law, was selling for a dollar or a dollar and a half, hot oil was selling for about thirty-five cents a barrel. Those cases were in many instances rather difficult to develop or prove. But they were such that it didn't take much evidence for a jury to convict the hot-oil runner of his wrong. In fact, it was nothing short of stealing.

A man called me at home one evening sometime about back in the middle '30s. He lived at Tulsa, Oklahoma, a man by the name of Lamb, a tall blond fellow, baldheaded, a very religious man, a devout Catholic. He came in and told me that I had been recommended to him as a good hot-oil lawyer. And that he wanted to sue a partner of his that he knew he was robbing him. To use his language, said, "He's stealing me blind." Said, "Now I don't have any evidence but I know he's running hot oil and he's not paying me for my part. I want to hire you and want you to file suit. I want you to hire investigators and I want you to sue him.

I accepted employment, hired an investigator, and right away commenced getting some evidence, most of it circumstantial, a large part of it rather weak. But when I finished, I had enough evidence that I was ready to try the case. I sued for some large amount of oil, probably a million barrels. I sued in federal court, in Judge Brown's court. Judge Brown appointed Judge Gordon Simpson, then practicing law at Tyler as special master, to take evidence in that hearing.

At the conclusion of a week's hearing, Judge Gordon Simpson made a report to the court finding that the evidence, while weak, was sufficient to support a judgment for two hundred thousand barrels of excess hot oil. And the court upon that recommendation rendered judgment in favor of Mr. Lamb for two hundred thousand barrels of oil.

The defense in that case was most unique. The defendant's lawyers contended that Mr. Lamb could not recover because that oil was contraband, that is, illegal. And oil produced in violation of the law is, under the Connally Act, contraband. You can't go out and legitimately sell it. But the courts turned a deaf ear to this defense, said the defendant himself can't make this oil contraband himself and then get behind that in the defense. It may be contraband but it's no defense to him in paying Mr. Lamb for his part of it. And the case was appealed to the Circuit Court of Appeals and heard at Fort Worth and they upheld Judge Brown's decision.

—L. L. James

Lease Dealer

Surprising, all types of people, from all walks of life, and from all parts of the country and from foreign countries, came into Ranger. I can't quote figures on it from memory, but I've been told that approximately thirty-five thousand came in there within one month's time that first month.

And I don't doubt it, because I distinctly remember there was no place for lots of them to sleep, no decent place for any of them to eat. I distinctly remember one individual who came there penniless; in fact, I loaned him one dollar out of my pocket, which to me in those days was a large sum of money. He told me that he was broke and he was hungry, and I never knew what it was to be hungry, but I didn't want to see anyone else go hungry, so I loaned him the one dollar. Six months later that man was a millionaire. He bought leases and royalties and sold them.

I don't know how he bought the first one; I never did learn, but I learned how he bought the others. For instance, I remember one day he went down to a little town south of Ranger, they called Hogtown; on the map I think it's Desdemona.

I know that he bought a lease down there. He gave a man a check for six thousand dollars. He had no money in the bank, or certainly he had no six thousand dollars in the bank. He came back to Ranger that night; it was after dark when he returned to Ranger, and he peddled that lease in the lobby of a Ranger hotel for fourteen thousand dollars and collected the money for it, or got a good certified check, either a certified or a cashier's check. Of course, the next morning when the bank opened he was there and deposited his money, long before the check he had given the day before had time to get in. And that's the way that man operated on that one particular deal.

I've known of cases very similar to that where men come in there not on a shoestring but on nothing, not even a shoestring. They started out, buying and selling leases and royalties, buying them as cheap as they could and selling them for as much as they could, and they made lots of money. And, of course, I've known others who came in there with a great deal of money and went away walking.

—John F. Rust

OIL-

FIELD

LINGO

8

Every industry develops a vocabulary of its own. Old terms may remain long after their original significance has been forgotten, but new devices and new techniques call for new names, and the men who operate the industry exercise their freedom of speech in naming or renaming the instruments and processes they employ. Thus catalytic cracking tower is shortened to cat; a heat exchanger used to prevent the gas choke from freezing is, because of its shape, called a watermelon; and a weight indicator equipped with a recorder that charts the weight at all times is called a stool pigeon, for if the well is shut down, it not only informs the tool pusher of that fact, but also tells him the exact time.

The cable-tool rig, developed by salt-well drillers before the birth of the oil industry, reflects its rural background. Bull as the first component in such compounds as bull wheel, bull rope, and bull tongs had the connotation of strength. The calf wheel performs a lighter task.

The oil worker's talk is filled with metaphors drawn from his occupation. One expression that dates back to horse-drawn transportation is spavined royalty. A spavined royalty is one that has been sold at a profit by several successive owners and has become so inflated in price that little or no chance of profit remains.

One of the misfortunes that can happen in rotary drilling is for the drill pipe to twist off in the well. To twist off, therefore, is to fail. If a worker fails to complete his straight in a poker game, he will throw his cards on the table and say, "I twisted off." If he tries to make a date with a girl and gets turned down, he will say, "I twisted off," unless his failure is due to another man's beating his time. Then he will say, "I've been drilled around."

To swab a well is to clean it out, and to swab a person is to try to get information out of him. A packoff is a device used to shut off the flow of water around a casing. To put the packoff on a person is to shut him up. To quit is to flange up, the last operation in connecting pipe. Pumpers are sometimes accused of not reading their gauges, preferring to remain in the comfortable boilerhouse and guess the contents of the tanks. Hence any kind of faked report or statistic is said to be boiler-housed.

As an industry becomes well known some of its terms pass into the general language. One thinks of by and large from the navigation of sail ships, of pan out from placer mining, and of maverick from the cattle industry. Wildcat seems to have reached a similar status, and many other oil-field terms have been granted the dignity of inclusion in dictionaries.

What follows is intended not as a glossary,* but rather as an

* The most exhaustive glossary yet published is Lalia Boone's *Petroleum Dictionary*, Norman: The University of Oklahoma Press, © 1952.

exhibition of some of the terms in context. It will be noted that some words have different connotations for different speakers.

BAND WHEEL (*see* Bull Wheel)

BOLL WEEVIL

They never called me boll weevil. Boll weevil wasn't in then. That was after we left West Texas, when they quit raising cotton. Some of the roughnecks were called boll weevils. A lot of them, oh, yes. Boll weevils, after the boom started. Boll weevils come in and they'd quit raising cotton, and they'd call them that. That's right, I've heard them call them that.

—Frank Redman

We called them boll weevils because they didn't know anything when they come. You see, they come right in off the farm. They didn't know a Stillson wrench from a pair of chain tongs. They didn't know that a screw in the right hand was to screw it in or the left hand to back it out. Well—you'd have to train him. By the time you had him trained, then he'd get chesty and get drunk and quit and work for somebody else. We had that trouble all the way through. Now the boys that stuck together more than any boys then was the boys that you could get out of your own home town, you see.

—W. H. (Bill) Bryant

Well, that [boll weevil] was an old saying, you know. A young fellow would come in from the farm or some town, boys going out in the field, why, they didn't want to have nothing to do, and he was a boll weevil. I know I was taking up a line when I was in the supply business that I bought from the Phillips Petroleum. It was out west or east of town here, known as the YMCA Survey, well number five, and they had about three thousand feet of line laying from that well. Why, I bought the casing to the well and this line, and I went and got an old-time pipe liner and told him I wanted to go out and take that line up. So I sent out about thirty-five men, and he worked a couple of hours, came over to me and told me, said, "I can't do a thing," said, "I'm just tied [*sic*]." I said, "What's the matter, LaRue?" And he said, "All boll weevils, all boll weevils." And he said, "I don't speak that boll-weevil language," and he said, "Now the only thing that I can say for you to do is go get Felix Reems," said, "Felix Reems is a boll weevil and he speaks the boll-weevil language."

So I got in the car and drove over and got Felix Reems and taken him out, and of course, the line came right on out. You see, he'd get along fine. You had to have a boll weevil that spoke the boll-weevil language, you see.

—E. L. Lantron

BOLL-WEEVIL DEVICE

And I'm not positive, but I think some man in Sour Lake invented what is called a blowout preventer or boll weevil, they used to call it. It was a lead seal that, when the pipe got to blowing too hard, that they could go down to their casing and set that in and around the casing. It was divided into two sections. Set that in down there, and that lead would seal it off, and of course, there was a pump and swivel that would have to hold the end of the drill stem. And that was his salvation until he got it [the well] killed. They usually killed them with clear water back in those days.

Back in those days, you know, Texas had quite a bit of cotton growing. Still does, for that matter. And a boy from the farm was referred to as a boll weevil because he was a cotton picker, you see, and maybe the boll weevils made a tramp out of him [by destroying the cotton] and sent him to the oil field. And, naturally, anything that was considered simple or essential, why they usually gave them such names as that. It was just a trifle. Anybody ought to have done it, you see. Didn't amount to nothing. They got to calling a steam lubricator—a homemade affair which was just a joint of pipe lowered a couple of inches lower than the steam line that went to the old single-cylinder engine, and anybody could pour oil in it—call that a boll weevil, because anybody could go out there and fill the lubricator. So they called that a boll weevil.

—Plummer M. Barfield

BOLL-WEEVIL STUNT

And one day he was on a drilling rig and hadn't worked there but a day or so till he lost two fingers in the crown block. Done a boll-weevil stunt, caught hold of the line and let it pull it in there. We always called them boll weevils, green-hand stuff, you know. We always called a green man a boll weevil.

—Benjamin Coyle

BOOMER

There's something peculiar about a boomer. He will be working on a good job and getting good wages and a good company, but if a boom starts someplace else, I have known them to quit good jobs, good positions, good living conditions, their families, and go to the boom. They couldn't tell you why. Part of the fever. It's a boom fever.

When the boom was over at Sour Lake, they came here, Saratoga, Spindletop. The next big boom after Batson was Humble. And they went there just in droves. Well, then after that, they went to Shreveport, when Louisiana come into the picture as an oil state, and they went up to Oil City. And every big boom after that, they went there until the last few years; they've reversed themselves. The boomers—I wouldn't term them boomers now, for when they've got a job, they'll stay with it. They want to stay away from the boom.

—James Donohoe

We was what I would call a different class of people from the boomers. And we went because we had a job and had to work there, see, and we made our living by working. But the boomers, they come in there, they were gamblers and highjackers and all such stuff as that—that's what we called the boomers. They was lots of them there.

—Bert Stivers

The psychology of the boomer is he's here today and yonder tomorrow, and little does he care what point it whistles. It doesn't make any difference to him just so he's got a place to sleep and something to eat. That's about what he's looking for, and if he's inclined to browse around, why, of course, that goes in the deal, too, and there's plenty of good whiskey along with that. That's the general type of those people, what you call general floaters, see. And there were a lot of them here. Plenty of them.

—James William Kinnear

A boomer is like this. You get into a field when it goes dead and the boys drift off and you feel no good. You know all your friends are over there in that field and you know there are a bunch of other guys over there. It's like going to the show. This field is dead here, there's no fist fightin', and drinking's kinda slack, and not much gambling. Town kinda civilized. Well, you go over there and probably you get in there and start running a rig, and there'll be another oil rig sitting off there, can't even hear the pump. Boy, when you get in there with a good rig, with probably thirty or forty rigs right around you and everyone trying to beat the other one, it's fascinating. All of them have them whistles on there, and when you start off there, all them whistles blow, trying to beat the other guy out of the hole.

—W. H. (*Bill*) *Bryant*

I don't know that I'd be considered a boomer, but I mean that we liked it where it was more exciting. Big new fields would come in, same company maybe. And the same people we knowed, they'd say, "Yeah, got a job for you at Batson." We'd go there, get sort of tired of this business of watching old pumping wells and greasing up the engines and looking after the stuff and gauging the tanks. We'd rather go to where the big doing's on, gang up there again.

I know when Humble first hit, why, they swarmed in there and no place to stay. They had the Crosby House, that Barney Doran ran, saloon and hotel, and one or two boardinghouses. But when they first came there—why, there was no place to sleep much. A fellow would come there looking for work a little ahead of time, and they'd sleep around the flare, gas flare, where the oil went through the separator and into the pit. They picked it up and put it into the stock tank. Why, the gas line went out into the lease there somewhere, and a six-inch pipe up in the air, and a big flame around it. They'd sleep around it to keep warm at night. Rangers came in there and arrested a lot of them as vagrants. They arrested them and chained them—march them into town and chain them to a tree.

—*Early C. Deane*

A boomer was the best mechanics there were. See, they traveled from shop to shop and learned all the tricks of the trade. Boilermakers, machinists, tinners, you know. Those days most of the shops were railroad shops, you know. And they'd go ride freight trains from one division to another, you know. Work till payday and then go to another. Always green grass ahead, you know.

—*Frank Redman*

BULL WHEEL

Well, there's bull wheels, there's calf wheels, there's band wheels. The band wheel was in the belthouse. The bull wheel was on the fartherest part of the derrick from the belthouse. Then the calf wheels—if you are using the calf wheels, they set in right close to where the driller stood there at the throttle and they used them when they drilled with cable tools. The calf wheels was to pull the pipe in or out or lower it; the bull wheels held the drilling cable to drill with. Then when you didn't use the calf wheels, when you were drilling, your block was thrown back over to one side, and you was drilling. When you had to run a string of pipe you got to keep it deep enough to run the string, or there was caving or something like that. So you would just throw the bull rope off and that calf wheel was run by clutch on the outside of the band-wheel shaft. You'd kick that clutch in and then you'd run your block up and down, pull your pipe, lower it, whatever you had to do.

—*Bert Stivers*

CALF WHEEL (see Bull Wheel)

CHRISTMAS TREE

You know what a Christmas tree is, don't you? Well, that's a blowout preventer, and they put two of them on most wells now just as a matter of course. They're capable of withstanding a hundred thousand pounds per square inch pressure. They're a complicated series of pipes, they stand up high, and they look like a Christmas tree, and that's why they call them a Christmas tree.

—*W. M. Hudson, Sr.*

Of course, the Christmas tree got its name having all those flares on it, you know. See, they'd come out with a main valve and put a four-way tree and come out four ways on that, and come up with another nipple, come out with a four-way tree and go up, and maybe reduce them down. Well, the modern Christmas tree now has got those spaces used for the chokes. In other words, a choke looks like a piece of two-inch pipe or a two-inch nipple to you—or three-inch, whatever the Christmas tree might be. But if it's a five-sixteenths, it's got a five-sixteenth hole in a solid piece of steel. And if it's a three quarters, it's got whatever size they put in it. In other words, they established a Christmas tree maybe with a thirty-second and a sixteenth and a five-eighth and a half inch. They'll try it at the various flows, you see. They don't have to change nothing. Their lines are all connected. They open the valve on three-sixteenths, and if it holds the right gas pressure—bottom and top-hole pressure, they call it—why, they'll flow it on the sixteenth. But if it don't, why, they'll just keep switching it around.

Now they've got these chokes already in there. All they've got to do is just shut this one off and move it up there until they establish the proper gas pressure. I forgot what the proper ratio is, but they got to have a certain amount of casing pressure, which is called bottom-hole pressure, to make a well flow regular with this modern scientific way they've got of flowing wells, which I think is wonderful because there's lots of fields that's been flowing ten years. Used to, they'd blow a head out in thirty days, and that was all. But now, with this modern pressure that they've figured out, why, they know how much pressure to have on the casing to keep so much pressure on the tubing to make a well flow; and some of them are flowing indefinitely. There's wells I know in this Gulf Coast been flowing ten years and still flowing. So they're bound to know what they're doing.

—*Plummer M. Barfield*

CRUMB BOSS

At that time, the individual producer, he never thought about taking care of his men, which I believe he ought to. But they never did. They just thought the old rough way. Just rough it, it was up to you. They didn't make any provision whatsoever for you.

But eventually oil companies and big corporations got to building bunkhouses. They had crumb bosses. He tended to all the making up the beds and everything, putting on the clean sheets whenever they had them. Well, some of those fellows would come in, didn't make any difference how old they was, they'd flop down on the bed, you know, and get to read a paper. So we got to calling them crumb bosses. That means louse, that's the byword for a louse.

—*Frank Hamilton*

DOODLEBUGGING

That lease is producing out of three or four different sands now and has been fully developed except in one sand. It now belongs to my boys, and I think they can live off that lease for the next fifty years. Understand, I don't recommend doddlebugging to anybody, but it just seems to work out for me better than most anything else, and it's very inexpensive, except the expense you use in drilling dry holes.

It's chemical. And we don't make much of it, and we don't except for our own personal use. I know it sounds foolish and absurd to take that position, but anything that has done as much for you as that has done for me, I just can't turn it down completely.

—*O. W. Killam*

FARMER'S SAND

Then there was always the joke about the farmer's sand. If you drilled a well and if it was a dry hole, you never went deep enough. Well, that became a joke in the oil country. By gosh, you never can drill to the farmer's sand. That's the sand that's so deep that you never drill to it, see. Well, by golly, John Farmer's sand has produced lots of oil. This deeper drilling has sure paid off. One thing, one reason we didn't drill, we didn't have the equipment to drill.

—*E. P. Matteson*

GANG PUSHER

The gang pusher is the one that run the engines and everything. Had charge of these other three men, you know. And he changed cups on them and pulled tubing and whatever we had to do; sometimes they'd form a leak in there, you know. We used standard valves then, and those standard valves were put in the ends of the barrels and just shoved up in there tight. There's a ball and seat in there, and when the pump lifts up, that lets the oil in.

—*Frank Hamilton*

LEASE HOUND

The fellow that got out and bought leases and traded in them was a lease hound. Then the operator, they called him a big shot. The average fellow out in the oil field—they didn't think much of a geologist. They called him "one of those scientists." "There comes another one of those scientist so-and-sos." They usually had something tacked onto practically all of 'em, you know.

—*Landon Haynes Cullum*

MAIL POUCHER

In the early boom in the little town of Electra, that field was about half and half rotary and cable tools, and there was lots of rivalry amongst the men. The cable-tool boys, they called the others swivel necks, and the swivel neckers, they called the cable gang mail pouchers.

They chewed Mail Pouch tobacco, most of the cable-tool gang; and to each of them, the other faction was a low-down sidewinder and they didn't get along so good. Finally the boardinghouses got to where they wouldn't mix them. They either went mail pouch or swivel neck—just a matter of keeping harmony.

—*E. P. Matteson*

When the weather was foggy—in other words, the fog was close to the ground—why you could smell that gas and it would be pretty strong. You were very careful about lighting a match, because for your own life, very careful. I know many of the men who were just about ready to strike a match and get a whiff of that gas and he'd quit right then, he wouldn't light it. The majority of the men who worked in the field in the early days did very little of that cigar smoking and cigarette smoking and even pipe smoking for this reason. They were warned and they knew in reason that if they lit that match why something might happen. And I tell you, Mail Pouch and different kinds of chewing tobacco—they sold millions and millions of pounds of it because the men went to chewing tobacco instead of smoking. Now that's what they did in those days.

—*Frank Dunn*

MUD DRINKER, MUD EATER

The cable-tool boys called the rotary boys a bunch of old mud drinkers; that's it, just a bunch of old mud eaters, because everything, you know, you drilled, you drilled with mud and water, and they called those the mud eaters.

—Landon Haynes Cullum

MUDDER

Come listen all you rounders;
    I'll tell you a tale that's sad.
All about a poor roughneck,
    And the troubles that roughneck had.
        He's a good old boy,
        But he's broke again.

Found him a mudder,
    And he asked for a meal.
Mudder said, "Where have you been working at?"
    And he told him, "In the oil fields,
        'Cause it's all I do
        'Cause it's all I do."

—Hardeman Roberts

NIGGER BOY

Now they have the nigger boy. That's an automatic gas fireman. You get your fires regulated, why, you can go to Fort Worth. You don't have to come back unless your water happens to be salty and foams on you. They called it nigger boy. See, anybody could do it. A nigger boy could do it, see?

—Plummer M. Barfield

OIL-FIELD DOVE

You'd have what you called these oil-field doves—the gals that hung around the oil fields, and there was plenty of them around. Of course, they all went under cover about thirty years ago or longer, but there were really some woollies, and they had all kinds of names for them. Some of them wouldn't be very good to repeat.

—Landon Haynes Cullum

OIL PAYMENT

There's one phase of the East Texas oil field that I want to mention because I do not think that it's very well understood by the laity—it's well understood among the oil fraternity. And that is the term "oil payment." When the East Texas field was first brought in, many wells were drilled for an oil payment. And many other things were bought for the oil payment—until there soon was floating around for sale in the East Texas oil field literally hundreds of oil payments.

An oil payment comes about in this way. A owns a lease on B's land. A wants to drill a well and he can't, so he hires C to drill the well and gives him thirty thousand dollars to be paid out of a certain fraction of the first oil to be produced from that well. It may be an eighth, it may be a quarter, it may be a half, any amount agreed upon, at whatever may be the price the oil brings. If oil brings a dollar a barrel, that is applied on that thirty-thousand-dollar oil payment until it is liquidated. And then the holder of that oil payment he's out; that interest reverts back to the lease owner.

Those oil payments were for sale over there during the years 1931, '32, and '33, anywhere from five cents on a dollar up to thirty-five cents on a dollar. An oil payment which would pay the money back in six months would sell for about fifty or seventy-five cents on a dollar. That means that a man that paid fifteen thousand dollars for a thirty-thousand-dollar oil payment would get his fifteen thousand dollars back in six months and then would have a fifteen-thousand-dollar profit to collect. An oil payment that would pay itself out in a year would sell for about twenty-five cents on a dollar. One that would pay itself out in two years about ten or fifteen cents on a dollar.

They were absolutely a good investment, just as safe as any investment. Because you'd ultimately get your money back. But people were even afraid of those. I had one client who at my recommendation bought many of those oil payments and got immensely rich. He bought those oil payments just hand over fist and as that money came in, he invested it in others and it just kept increasing. And he's a very rich man today on account of those oil payments he bought.

—L. L. *James*

PENCIL PUSHER

We had what they call oil scouts—we called them pencil pushers —coming around all the time. They wanted to know how deep you was and what formation you was drilling in and all this sort of thing and that. And I usually give them very little information because we always made logs of our wells, which when I made one I very seldom showed it to any of those fellows. I showed it to the fellows I was drilling for. Scouts for other companies and this and that, you know. Just nosing around trying to get information.

I furnished them, like I said, when I drilled such wells as that White Point well and all those wells in that part of the country, I furnished the geologists with all the information that you might say they ever needed. They didn't have to have much more. They tried to give themselves credit for a lot of it, but I didn't care if they did. It didn't cost me anything.

—W. D. Bowen

POOR-BOY

Dad Joiner seemed to be obsessed with the almost unbelievable deep conviction that he was certainly going to find oil in that area. And he wasn't to be balked at making two failures but simply skidded the derrick over a few hundred feet and proceeded with the drilling. He had no money and financed the drilling of those wells by borrowing, begging, selling interests, leases, royalty, or any way in the world that he could get hold of a dollar. He simply poor-boyed those wells down.

HAYES: Mr. James, you've used the term "poor-boy" two or three times. As I understand it, "to poor-boy a well" is to go in without any finances at all and beg, borrow, or otherwise get your hands on enough money to do your drilling. And sometimes you have to borrow other equipment as you go from place to place in the field and any time you find a driller who is willing to help you out with either equipment or labor and does so, why that all figures in the term "poor-boy." Is that right?

JAMES: That's right. That's the picture exactly. It's simply drilling an oil well without any money and getting the means any way you can.

HAYES: And a good many of them are drilled that way?

JAMES: Yes, many of them are drilled that way. And when an oil field comes in, the oil-field wildcatters and lawsuit hunters and lease hounds and royalty buyers, they flock in there. And some fellow that hasn't got a dollar is always ready to enter into a contract to drill a well for somebody. And then he hopes to go out and rent his rig on a credit and pay for it with bottom-hole money and hire his crew and buy his fuel oil and his derrick and all that, all on the credit, hoping that he'll luck out. Sometimes they do and most of the time they didn't because they just couldn't do it. They got too deep in debt before they got the well completed.

—L. L. James and R. M. Hayes

PUSHER (*see also* Gang Pusher)

The pusher was the leader of the roustabouts. He's the one, when you had what we call a well off—it wasn't pumping—he stood there and watched us take off the saddles, take the walking beam off, stop it. He took care of the engine. When we start using the elevators to pull the tubing or the rods, he was the master of the engine. He run the engine and you did the other work. But he was the master, he told you what to do, how to do and what they were going to do. And that's the reason why they call him the roustabout pusher.

—Frank Dunn

ROPE CHOKER

The rope chokers were the cable-tool boys, you know. And the toolie—they called the tool dresser the toolie. There's so many of those terms you just forget all of 'em. You forget after a while.

—Landon Haynes Cullum

ROUGHNECK

A roughneck is one who looks after the breaking out of the pipe, stacking of the pipe, and the derrick work. He didn't have the amount of work the roustabout did. He just looked after what I'm telling you.

—Frank Dunn

A roughneck was just a fellow like that boy told that judge, just stout in the back and weak in the head. But nevertheless, like a bookkeeper I had said about it, he said, "They can't organize them. A roughneck's not a laboring man." And I said, "Why?" He says, "They're diplomats. They don't do like any other working people ever I saw in my life anywhere. They can confuse you."

I said, "Why?" And he said, "After World War I here, you walk in a tool house and there'd be silk shirts hanging everywhere, good clothes and everything else, and when the panic hit, they just went on. They just forgot all about the silk shirts and one thing and another. It don't worry them. That's just over the hill—that is, that's down the river for them. They can come back; they can just adapt themselves better than anybody in the world."

—*Benjamin Coyle*

ROUSTABOUT

A roustabout means this: that he looks after the wells, see that they are pumping, or if they need repairs. The roustabout looks after the storage tanks. He goes to the storage tanks, and each one of the wells has what they call discharge line from the well. Each one was separate so you could tell whether a well was pumping or not. From there he looked after the neatness of the field, that is, he picked up different broken rods, junk pipe, different connections. In other words, kept it so you wouldn't have any danger of stumbling over when you'd be working on a well.

He dug ditches to take care of the waste water, the salt water that would be accumulated into the stock tanks, that went to a certain pit. They tried to evaporate that in many different ways. They built fires to evaporate the water because they had no special place to take care of that water. The roustabout looked after that.

The roustabout looked after any repairs that should be made to the derrick. From that they went on then to the boilers. They washed boilers, they see that the boilers were properly taken care of, that is, the tubes were swabbed. Then the mainways were taken out and seen that they didn't accumulate any salt. From that they went on to the discharge lines, which developed every now and then a leak which was caused by salt water eating up the pipe. From that part of it on they went on then to gauge every so often how much the wells were pumping. In other words, if they had different royalty owners and they provided a tank for a certain well, they had to see about how much that well was doing by itself. In other words, each royalty owner got what the wells that were drilled on that acreage.

A roustabout looked after the steam engine, the amount of oil that was pumped from each well, gauged it each day, see that the wells were kept up, see that the machinery didn't have any knocks in the bearings, the band wheel, the eight-inch belt that took care of the band wheel; looked after the beams to see that they were well oiled and greased, in other words the bearings that the band wheel had and also the beam, which had special boxes, oil boxes. They used grease instead of oil on them. They had to be looked after. When the well would be pulled, they pulled out a broken sucker rod that was laid aside. Then there was new clamps put on that and reriveted to take care of another one that might happen to other wells. They would have them in advance. That was another roustabout duty. They got the name of the roustabout because they had so many things to do.

—*Frank Dunn*

SCISSORS BILL (*see* Starved Owl)

SNAKE

There used to be a fellow name of Rogers I used to work with, dressed tools for him. He's a great fellow to make up songs, you know, and sing 'em. He made one up called the "West Virginia Snake." I'd always laugh when he'd sing it, you know. He'd sing about ten or fifteen verses of it, you know. It started off like:

Right smart, tolerable like,
I reckon, workin' by the hour;
A bag of meal, a box of snuff,
The real old short stuff,
Likewise a sack of flour.
Where the snow comes down in flakes.
We'll roam up the mountain,
We are the boys that fears no danger.
We are the West Virginia snakes.

That's one verse of it. I got that much out of my memory. Yes, the West Virginia oil workers all called themselves snakes, you know. You know, that's a great copperhead country.

–C. C. *McClelland*

STARVED OWL, SNAKE, SNAKE HUNTER

There was a shortage of drillers and this Ranger boom come on and a great deal of the oilmen wanted Pennsylvania and West Virginia drillers, but in later years many of the native Texans developed into drillers just as efficient or more efficient than many of the older men were—did not have the old customs to handicap them, had a different way of thinking.

It seems strange to me now that we used to think that if you weren't from a certain state you never could be an efficient worker. Oil first started out in Pennsylvania in 1859, when all of our original oilmen like Gib Morgan and those other characters, were Pennsylvanians, local Pennsylvanians. Then as these booms played out they came down into West Virginia. They had to contend with the natives of West Virginia and called them snake hunters—said they had to hunt snakes for a living—and West Virginians called them "starved owls," because they used to have to come to West Virginia to make a living, and there were many fights.

Then as many generations of West Virginians grew up, they went to work in other states and then they—together with the Pennsylvanians—would have contempt for the other workmen. I can remember when I went to Illinois just as a seventeen-year-old boy hearing the oilmen talking about the scissors bills, as they called the natives from Illinois. They said, "You cannot learn these dumb fellows anything. They are too dumb to learn. They are just thickheaded. They cannot learn anything." I never stopped to think. I believed it, too. I never stopped to think that the descendants there —those people from Illinois or most of them—came from old Virginia and had came south down through the Cumberland Gap and then into Kentucky, Indiana, and Illinois.

Then you come to Texas, and you would hear the same kind of talk about these native Texans down here. "Never learn them anything." The most efficient workers we had learned the business here in Texas, and were down here when these booms first started off in this part of the country.

–O. G. *Lawson*

SWIVEL NECK (*see* Mail Poucher)

TANK STRAPPER

Gaugers' duties were to go up there and gauge this oil. See, we had two-hundred-and-fifty-barrel tanks and we had to take a sample of it, bring it out, sift machines to see BS & W [basic sludge and water] in it, get the gravity. It's just the same as they would get the gravity on whiskey. You probably used a stick down there and it'd give you the gravity of the oil. We had tickets, we kept a copy of them and give this other man, he'd sign it, the pumper, he'd have to sign it, you see. And he'd give you a number for it; for instance, a five-hundred-barrel tank would run thirty-two barrels to a foot. And he'd had to strap the tank; they had a regular strap tank, a man that strapped the tank himself. They'd use the Robinson Table. They still use it on strapping a tank.

He measured the circumference of the tank, the height of it and the center of it, and he figured; he got a table that showed you, for instance, like you're taking a reading on a gas well. You take an open flow of a gas well there was on a spring gauge, why you put it right over to the edge and whatever registered on this spring gauge, why, you had a table, supposed to be the most accurate, which all the companies recognize, and you turn that arrow right there to how many pounds register on the spring gauge and it'd give the number of feet of gas that it made in one hour.

—*Frank Hamilton*

THIEF

A thief in those days was twelve inches long and it was two inches square, had a glass in the front of it which had the inches right down the side of the glass. And that glass was put in there. It had a trap door on the bottom, a chain and a trip cord. When you lower that to the bottom you hit the bottom of the tank. You raise it up one inch, you measured it to see that it was only one inch. Then you tripped that latch and it closed. You pulled the line up. You wiped off the face of the glass and when you did the oil and the water would be divided. You had so much water and the rest was all oil. If you had six inches of oil you raised it up one inch, you had five inches of oil. It showed just as plain as you looked out the glass, more especially if you put plenty of soap on that glass on the inside, and on the outside the water would be just as straight across as if you cut it with a knife. And it was perfect—a perfect thief and a perfect gauge.

They called it a thief because the water and the oil was two different things. If they pumped water out with that oil you were a thief with it.

—Frank Dunn

TOOLIE (*see* Rope Choker)

YELLOW DOG

I've run at night over there, and we didn't know what to generate or what, and we'd never handled electric lights like the boys had. We had what we call a yellow dog. Now, a yellow dog is like a tea kettle, only it has a spout on each end. Well, you take oakum and run it through and around, you see, till you fill those up, and then you cut it in two and come on around and pour it full of coal oil. You have one in the derrick and one on the floor. Well, when the well is going to make gas, we couldn't have it because it would set the rig afire, you see. And I have run all night and never seen a man. I'd make one sit down by me, where I could put my hand on him. Run all night long there in the dark—make all your connections in the dark.

—W. H. (Bill) Bryant

HAZARDS

OF

THE

GAME

9

Viewed in retrospect, the oil industry of the first years of this century seems unduly wasteful not only of oil and gas but of human life as well. What the toll of human life was cannot be determined with certainty, and in relation to man-hours worked it was probably no greater than it was in lumbering and mining. As in other expanding industries the primary consideration was to get the job done in the quickest way. Safety, however, was never totally disregarded—witness the headache post on the earliest drilling rigs. Yet some equally simple devices were slow in coming. For many years drive ropes and chains, sprockets and gears were left exposed. The derrick man stood on a small open platform sixty or more feet above the ground. When safety belts were introduced, many men refused to use them, fearing that they would delay escape in case of fire or an eruption of gas. The elevators for raising and lowering pipe were equipped with a simple hook, easily jarred loose.

When wells were drilled in they were permitted to flow unchecked as a means of cleaning them out. There was no effective blowout preventer. Men without gas masks capped flowing wells, using steel tools that might cause a spark. There were no steel helmets to protect heads from objects dropped from the derrick or steel-toed shoes to protect the feet.

Fire-fighting equipment was almost nonexistent. So was any kind of fire control. Workers carried lighted lanterns and struck matches for pipes and cigarettes where gas might ignite in smothering flame. Lightning at any time could strike open wooden or earthen tanks. Nothing had been invented that would control a well spewing forth in flame. Poisonous gas collected in low areas, and there was no warning of its presence.

There are many reasons for this lag in safety, among them the persistence of attitudes of a previous generation. The nineteenth century had been a venturesome one; and casualties, whether the victims were settlers on the frontier, passengers on a Mississippi River steamer, cowboys on the trail, or crews of derailed trains, were regarded as the price of progress. Employers were not completely exempt from legal responsibility for death and injury to their workmen, but until the states enacted liability laws, a common-law defense might be made on the ground that the worker at the time of his entry into the contract was aware of the danger and freely assumed the risks involved. The early workmen's compensation acts passed by the various states offered limited protection and perhaps helped turn attention to accident prevention.

As the selections that follow show, oil executives differed widely in their acceptance of responsibility for the safety of their men. Some were backward, others in advance of their time. If the new Texas companies appear more generous, it is perhaps because they were

13. An oil field crew in the Sour Lake-Batson-Saratoga area, about 1904.
—"The Oral History of Texas Oil Pioneers," *Texas University Library*

14. Lake of oil from flowing wells, Humble, Texas, about 1905.
—"The Oral History of Texas Oil Pioneers," *Texas University Library*

15. Digging an earthen storage tank, Humble, Texas, about 1905.
—"The Oral History of Texas Oil Pioneers," *Texas University Library*

16. Before the time of automobiles and all-weather roads, a workman necessarily lived near his work. When oil was found, the normal housing development was from "Ragtown" (tents) to "Shacktown" (cheap wooden shacks) to more permanent housing for those who remained after the boom. The Texas Company in 1909 provided tents for a crew drilling a wildcat well between Sour Lake and Saratoga. The man seated in the opening of the tent is Max T. Schlicher, a part of whose memoirs appears on page 84.—*Max T. Schlicher*

17. Rotary rig crew in an early Texas oil field.
—"The Oral History of Texas Oil Pioneers," *Texas University Library*

ON THE "HIGHWAY" IN THE FAMOUS BURK-WAGGONER OIL POOL

18. A big parade of oil field equipment moves through the Burkburnett Field of Texas in 1919, the scene of one of the discoveries that made the Southwest the nation's great producing center.—*Library of Congress*

19. Fire at Harrell No. 7, Caddo, Louisiana, showing Civil War cannon used by the Sharp brothers in their attempt to shoot the fire out. —"The Oral History of Texas Oil Pioneers," *Texas University Library*

20. When a new field was opened, there was the problem of what to do with the oil until storage tanks could be erected, pipe lines laid, and refineries built. One answer was the earthen tank. The one shown here was at Humble. Waste was somewhat reduced by floating the oil on water. —"The Oral History of Texas Oil Pioneers," *Texas University Library*

21. The surprising thing about this early photo of the main street of Newtown, Texas (otherwise known as Mud Lane, Waggoner City), is that cars somehow managed to negotiate the quagmire. The baths behind the misnamed Palace Barber Shop must have done a rushing business! Newtown was an oil boom "city" of the early 1920s.—*Humble Oil and Refining Company*

22. A cable-tool rig in use about 1920. By then, most drilling was done by rotary rigs. —*Drilling Magazine*

23. The Breckenridge, Texas, oil field, 1920. Horses were still used to haul oil field equipment.—*American Petroleum Institute*

24. Tuckertown, Navarro County, Texas, in the early 1920s. Growth from nothing to a population of 6000 in three months.
—"The Oral History of Texas Oil Pioneers," *Texas University Library*

25. C. M. ("Dad") Joiner, third from left, discovered the largest oil field in the United States, the East Texas Field, in 1930. He had started drilling in the area in 1927, at the age of seventy, and kept trying for three years, although geologists and other oilmen predicted he would find only dry holes. Toward the end, his funds were so low that he fueled his boilers with scrub pine. The man who is congratulating Dad Joiner at the discovery well—Daisy Bradford No. 3—is A. D. Lloyd, a geologist.
—*Texas Mid-Continent Oil and Gas Association*

small and the executives, many of whom had come up from the ranks, knew their men personally.

Protests from the workers were rare. In all these interviews there is no instance of a worker's refusing to obey an order because of danger. They felt they had a job to do, and risk did not deter them. Moreover, many of them liked the excitement of danger. Perhaps at a later time they would have been race-car drivers; they took pride in proving themselves men in a sense in which pencil pushers and counter jumpers were not. They proved themselves, and the oil fields were filled with legends of brave men who survived or who died making the brave attempt.

Death Warrant

I started to work on the sixteenth day of May 1902, and I was seventeen years old on the thirty-first of May. They gave me a death warrant—what they called a death warrant in those days—to sign. It read that I am a white man, twenty-one years old of age, realize that the work is dangerous, and assume all risk. That was in May; in September my brother came down. He was two years older than I was, and they wouldn't let him work because he was too young. He asked too many questions before he signed the paper.

They never used it in a lawsuit or anything. I don't know why. It was supposed to be a bluff more than anything else, a protection from being sued. Most of the companies took very good care of their regular men; all the stable companies did, always had. So far as I know, the native companies and the Sour Lake companies always done that. Our company always carried a man, if he was considered a regular employee, on the payroll, if he was sick, at least four or five months. People not on the regular payroll would not be taken care of unless they were injured on the job; then they were taken care of. Passing the hat to help a man or his family in need was regular, and the oil-field worker was always very liberal with him.

—R. R. *Hobson*

Age of Innocence

The most dangerous work I ever done in the oil field was working on a big gusher was brought in in 1916 in the Goose Creek field. There was crowds of people, when they heard about the gusher, rushed to Goose Creek to see it. And they was standing around anywhere from fifty to seventy-five yards from the well, and we had very few guards, if any, out to keep them from striking matches and starting a fire. Seems that we didn't even realize at the time that we were in as much danger as we were. We were lucky we didn't have a fire.

We were working under—we were just saturated with oil—just a gusher going to the top of the derrick, and falling back on us— working there trying to cap that well. At the same time, we didn't realize it was so dangerous. We even had the boiler—firing a boiler within seventy-five yards of us. And today they wouldn't think about doing a thing like that, but we did at that time. So I think by far that that was the most dangerous thing that I ever done in the oil field. We didn't have a fire. If we had had a fire, I wouldn't be here to tell about it.

—*James W. Riggs*

Narrow Escape

I've some very narrow escapes by things falling out of the derrick. I had a sucker-rod elevator one time to fall, and it hit me on the arm. It was a glancing lick, and if it had hit me on the head or anyplace else, it would have killed me right now. And then I've had several close calls at other work in the field, but fortunately for me that I didn't have any accidents serious enough to cause any bones to [be] broke or have to be sent to the hospital or laid up with a long sick spell.

—*James Donohoe*

The Crown Block Came Down

We had one of our drillers killed—Bert Rambeau. He was a good driller and a good man, but he was a little wild in pulling casing and tubing and he was stuck. And he was pulling a well for—I forget the name of the company now that he was working for. He quit us boys and was drilling that well and he got stuck. And the boys all got away from him. He had a good crew of men and they got back and says, "Now, Bert, be careful there." He kept a-heaving and a-heaving and he says, "Well, if the crown starts in, why I'll get out of the way." He just turned the engine wide open and give it all

the power, and pretty soon in come the crown block. Well, he made
a run and had got nearly out of the reach of that timber that fell
towards him, and hit him on the head and killed him dead as an
Indian, and he never did know what hit him—Bert Rambeau.

That was one of the boys that was killed on Spindletop and
there were several others out there that got wounded pretty bad.
Now, Claude Deer fell off of a cistern out there. He went up to look
into it and his foot give away and he went over backwards and broke
his leg there. And several others got a pretty hard bump. My brother
at one time got knocked out for a little while. He was letting in the
tubing or casing, whichever it was, and the lever on the brake was a
long bar of iron that stuck out about five or six feet. Well, that would
come up as high as your head. If you happened to be in the way of
it, it would knock you down or split your head open. Well, he was
standing a little too close and it hit my brother in the head and just
knocked him out. It didn't hurt him bad, it just barely touched him.

—*William Joseph Philp*

Don't Crawl through the Bull Ropes

The first accident I ever had was on the fifth of July, I don't
know what year it was now, but there was just three of us working
in the gang. One fellow—I called him Kelly, all I ever knew, just
Kelly—that's a nickname for him—he stepped through the bull ropes
one day when the engine was running. When I got where I could
stop, I told him, "Now, Kelly, don't you never step through them
bull ropes when this engine's running. You git killed that way or
hurt." He said he'd stepped through them a hundred times. I said,
"Yeah, you're gonna step through them one too many. Don't you
do it when I'm running this engine. That's one thing I don't allow."

So Fourth of July come, we's off. Went back on the fifth, went
down, pulled a well. Got all the rods back in the hole but three
fourbles—you know, that's four rods together. So I went to pull one
up to reverse my engine, and my reverse lever broke. I said, "Grab
the brake, Kelly." Instead he just made a dive through them bull
ropes and as he went through, he fell and his pants leg caught what
they call the dog on the bull wheel that helps to throw the bull
ropes on. Caught his pants leg and carried him right between the
bull wheel post and the bull wheel and brought him around and
throwed him up through the cross of the derrick, where he come

down and his shoulders hit right on these bull ropes. Bounced up and fell right down on the casing head, right on the floor. Well, he was out for a pretty good while.

So the doctor and the superintendent got out there, this man Rith, this superintendent, says, "Bill, how in the world did you carry that man around that bull wheel and didn't kill him?"

Well, I says, "Mr. Rith, come in here and I'll show you." We's right at another well, so I went in there and showed him, told him all about it, just how it happened.

He says, "Well, I couldn't imagine how that thing happened. But I see now. Lot of funny things can happen in an oil field, can't they?"

I says, "Yeah." So we went back and the doctor was examining him. I says, "Doctor, he may have a broken collarbone; he fell right down on the rope. His ankle—he's got a skinned elbow. He hit that foot with his elbow as it was carrying him through there. I just stepped back out of the way and watched it; I couldn't do nothing else."

And he mashed on this fellow, and he says, "Ohhhhh."

"Yes, you one-eyed son of a bitch, Bill told you not to step through them ropes."

I couldn't help but laugh; I's sorry for the fellow.

Lots of people got hurt, oh, Lordy. Lots of men got killed or crippled up uncalled for. Through ignorance, a lot of it, and through unsafe equipment too, you know. Most of the accidents could be avoided, but people were ignorant of the danger and they'd just take chances. And your equipment wasn't safe like it is now, not at all. Nowadays they've got elevators that you could drop a string of tubing and it wouldn't come off. Same way when you hook one, why it's hooked; it won't come unhooked. Them days was just plain old things, you know, nothing—it was a hard go. And then one man as an average knows about as much as another, and they all had to learn it, you know. And it made it a little bit tough that way.

—*Bill Ingram*

I've Seen Men Fall

I've seen men fall from a derrick and I've seen them come down the guy wire to escape a blowout and escape the fire which happened immediately afterwards.

I had a man killed when I was a contractor at Jonesville. Had a man fall only about fifty feet and die from it. Seen other men fall from the thribble board and live, fall on the derrick floor—broken arm. Some of them fall from a small, short distance, and the way they hit injured their spine or internal injuries and they die. Others can fall a good ways.

I saw a man jump from a derrick at Spindletop that was falling. This derrick had been snubbed to and was bossed by a man that pulled the wells. The derricks was so close together at Spindletop, if you didn't have pulling equipment with a standard rig, or bobtail rig, or hoisting outfit of your own, you'd hire a man that had a hoisting station near there, and he'd run lines to your derrick to pull rods or tubing if necessary. He'd have to run it through snatch blocks till he got to your place, and have a man or two to signal —rather hazardous all the time in pulling.

In this particular case, he pulled this leg out from under this derrick that was over the well that I was superintendent for, that was pumping with a steam head. That lease was only eleven feet by twenty-two, and we'd have to hire pulling machines to pull the well, or hoist, because we had no room for it. And it pulled this derrick over, and derricks was so close together, that when it fell it knocked down two others. In the second one there was a man up on the double board, and I saw him run. And instead of running away from the derrick—our derrick falling and hitting his—why, he ran towards it.

And I said, "Why, the big sucker, he's going to get killed sure." But he was smart. As it fell over, he jumped into a slush pit and was saved. He was all right and wasn't hurt at all.

The men weren't careless, but some of them were reckless. They'd get irritated if pipes stuck, and they'd hit it too hard. They'd back off the engine and run and hit it too hard, instead of taking a steady pull. Sometimes they'd pull in the derrick that way and hurt men.

But they were usually pretty careful, because a driller that was in charge, he'd been a roughneck too, and knew the dangers of it all. He'd try to look out for his men. If he was pulling on stuck pipe, he'd have his men get away off the derrick till he needed them for something.

I saw one man killed at Hoskins Mound. He was irritated and run off and hit it too hard, and just pulled the derrick in on himself, with no other men on the floor. He had his neck broken and died.

It was a long ways away from a doctor; it was twenty-five miles to Alvin, I think, in horse and buggy. We tried to revive him, but when the doctor got there, he said he'd been dead a long time, said he had his neck broken.

—*Early C. Deane*

Boiler Explosions

I had several boiler explosions while I was there. One boiler, the center boiler of a battery of five, exploded once and the fireman was standing on the boiler for some reason. It must have been a dry boiler and he must have turned some water in through some stopcock he opened, and the boiler exploded, and they found one of his legs about forty feet up in the derrick, hanging in the derrick. Just scattered him all over the countryside. And another boiler explosion —across the road from a friend of mine's house, an old man. I don't even know what he did, but I know that I visited him every time I went by his shack. This boiler exploded and took a jump of about a hundred feet in the direction of his house, and as it came over, one of the flues came out of the boiler and went diagonally through the door of his house and didn't splinter the wood, a two-inch flue, just a hole went through diagonally through his house, and the old man was sitting at his table and it went over one eye. The flue was stuck up his eye, and his brains dropped out the end of the flue.

—*W. M. Hudson, Sr.*

When the Shell Comes Back

I had an interesting experience on the first well I drilled out there [on the Fred Thom lease]. Tom Mendenhall came out to shoot it and there was quite a bit of gas in the well and we loaded a six-foot bucket with liquid nitroglycerin and were letting it down on top of another bucket that was already in the hole. The six-inch bucket that was in the hole, I guess, squeezed the gas a little bit, and it made a blanket or a pocket in there, and when we let this second bucket down, the gas just caught it and began to push it back up.

Well, of course, the only thing I could think of was the tall uncut. I never was a speed demon, but I figured I'd try to make a new track record. Tom was standing right by the well. And he put his head down and he could hear this glycerin bucket scraping on the side of the casing as it came up and he said, "Don't run off, Walter. I'll take care of it." And so old foolish me, I stood there to see what he was going to do, and he did something I wouldn't do at all. He just spread his legs out on each side of the top of the casing and waited until this bucket of liquid glycerin came right up. And when it got up about waist-high, he reached over and hugged it like he was coming home to Mama.

That well, after it was shot, only produced forty or fifty barrels a day.

—*Walter Cline*

We'll All Get Fired

The funniest experience that I ever had in this seismograph work happened up here by Garber. We had an explosion—what we called a premature explosion. The way we loaded this dynamite in these seismograph holes, we had what we called the tamp. It was merely a hinged rod that would go—well, our holes usually run sixty feet—and it had a copper spoon on the end of it that we'd tie these two-and-a-half-pound sticks of dynamite. They were two inches in diameter and sixteen inches long and we'd tie them on this spoon and push them to the bottom of the hole, and of course, the number of trips you had to make depended on the size charge you were going to fire.

Well, this particular hole had filled up with sand and we cleaned it out, started down with our charge, and we lost it about fifteen feet down. Well, the sand packed around it and we couldn't get the charge up or down, so we started by it with another charge and it exploded. I happened to be the one that was loading the hole, and the force coming out of that hole picked me up, oh, I would guess about three or four feet in the air and pushed me, just slammed me back against a bank by the hole there and I was hanging on that bank kind of like a picture, only I wasn't hanging on a nail, the pressure was holding me up there.

Of course, it was all over with right quick. Seemed to me like it was quite a while, but then in reality it was a matter of seconds. And the small gravel and dirt came out with such force and hit me in the face and on the neck to where I carried what they didn't pick out, the sand and gravel, in my neck for several days, because it just drove it into the hide. And the funny part of it was the chief operator came running down there and run up to me and asked me if I was hurt and luckily I wasn't, but I was scared. I guess I didn't talk very plain to him or something and he stood there and looked at me a minute and said, "My God, don't die, we'll all get fired."

We used sixty per cent dynamite, which means sixty per cent nitroglycerin. According to the information that the dynamite companies gave us, it'd take forty-pound pressure per square inch before it would go off without the cap. Of course now, the cap, it required very little pressure. I remember one incident. We had a discussion whether or not you could hang a piece of dynamite out on a stick and shoot it with a .22 rifle, whether it would go off or not. It will definitely go off when you shoot it with a rifle, but you can put a pile of it out there scattered out on the ground, not pile it up, and it'll burn just like gasoline.

                                                        —W. C. Wigley

I Didn't Have Any Feeling

There was a fellow by the name of Hickok was the shooter there; and they had magazine down there in the hollow. It was real cold weather. Hickok and two other fellows went up there to fix up the stove in the magazine, to thaw the glycerin out, you know. And some way or other it just went out.

Well, we were sitting up on the hill, in the boilerhouse, waiting to get gas for the well where we's drilling. So when that thing went up, it just, you know, jumped us right up off the seat while we was down there. And this Hickok—he told it afterwards—he was outside of this magazine and the other two fellows was in. And he had a saw, sawing wood, and had a fork of a tree, and he was sawing with this handsaw, this wood, to build a fire in the stove, when it went up.

Actually I never saw anything like that. Now he had a necktie on, and that necktie hung down about here, and it just looked like chipped glass hanging down there, and it blowed the whole back of his trousers out, clear out; blowed his shoes off his feet, and his head was just full of tin. We pulled a lot of it out. Then they took him to Pittsburgh to the hospital. He got all right.

After he got well, you know, he come back, and I said to him, "George, how'd you feel when that thing blowed up?"

"Feel?" he said. "There was nothing to feel; I was numb. I didn't have any feeling."

And I said, "Did you realize you was alive?" He said yes, he did.

—C. C. McClelland

It Would Make You Blind

The first well at Sour Lake was brought in by the Texas Company, and it came in just oozing with that terrible gas pressure. Now this gas was poison. It was awful dangerous and you had to watch it at nights. At the time I was pumping three wells with steam—we all had steam, had steam boxes, and I was pumping these three wells then—and we had to watch this gas because the atmosphere was heavy and it would get close to the ground and look like smoke. And you had to lay down on the ground. We generally wet our handkerchief and put it over our nose to keep from getting that gas in our lungs.

And I know a man by the name of Jack Finnigan and a boy that died one night in there. We found him the next morning trying to get to the water. It also made you blind, get blind in your eyes. I was blind myself for twenty-one days.

And it looked like it didn't affect your eyes a bit after you got over it. We'd use Irish potatoes to put on our eyes, but this time, by golly, I had to go to Galveston and open up my eyes up under water, and, eventually, why I got to where I could see all right, just kind of dim at first. Stayed in a dark room all the time.

—Frank Hamilton

You Just Had to Try to Hold Your Breath

All of those domes had that sulphuric gas was poisonous. Spindletop, Sour Lake, Saratoga, Batson, and Humble were poisonous gas. And I've been knocked out with it twice. I was blind there for quite a while. If you got two or three good whiffs of it it just knocked you out. I was knocked out with it. It was at Batson. We were trying to put connections on a well that had come in. We didn't have any gas masks then. You just had to try to hold your breath if you was in it till you could step out and breathe. Get two or three good breaths of it, why, you just went blind and went out. Those days and times they didn't control; all your gas flowed. It flowed through a separator, a cylindrical tank, and was burned. Nowadays it's all controlled and used.

—J. A. Rush

We'd Just Take a Chance

Well, the wells were shallow [on the Shoestring district at Sour Lake], and they drilled them pretty fast. Rained a great deal; mud on the ground was a handicap. But they'd haul in and we'd wade in through it, and they brought in the wells one after the other pretty fast.

The gas from this oil was—I think it was sulphurous-acid gas. It would asphyxiate you; it would knock you out. There wasn't much safety provision those days. We'd just take a chance. But when the wells would come in, they'd let them blow up over the derrick. Silly, of course, a waste and dangerous. But also the foggy atmosphere with the damn deadly gas, and in some cases we'd keep one man on the ground, while we were pulling out the drill pipe, and a derrick man up in the derrick. Keep one man on the ground to watch other wells. He'd let out a yell now and then, "Hughes bringing in Number two. Come down out of there."

This fellow would come down out of there till they got her shut in because they was just falling all over the place, and some men didn't escape.

Walter Sharp always had the welfare of his men at heart. And he and I guess Jim or some of them, they designed or bought a helmet that was used in mine disasters, I think. And in one case that I remember seeing, they brought it down, and old Tom Smith volunteered to go in and get this man out. He was lying there apparently dead, on back a hundred yards, I guess, back behind the Texas Company line, back in the Shoestring Strip. They then tied a rope around Tom Smith's waist, in case he got knocked out, and he made his way through the mess of pipe lines and stuff there and derricks to this man there. Put him on his shoulder and carried him out. They revived him by artificial respiration, I guess it was. We got him on his feet and going all right. And that was quite a valuable experience to us.

That helmet we used afterwards. I don't know what it had in it

or anything, or whether it had oxygen or what. Tom Smith wasn't
knocked out, and for which we were all glad.

—*Early C. Deane*

The Lightning Strikes

The real fire was in Batson Prairie when those big tanks caught
fire from lightning.

They built those big underground tanks. That was before the
days they got to building so many iron tanks because they were too
costly, and they couldn't get the steel. They were probably fifteen
feet deep and maybe a hundred yards square. Then they pumped
about a foot or so of water in the bottom, and this oil would ride
on this water. Well, they covered these over with planks, and they
left a funnel in the top for this gas to go out. And they didn't realize at that time that was a perfect trap for that—point right
straight up at the clouds.

Well, when the storm got up there and got close enough for
them to form a complete circuit, why, bam, goes down, and the
thing explodes and sets the fire. That burned up two million and
seven hundred and fifty thousand barrels of oil. Burned up there.
I believe it was about ten of those big tanks burned.

The first day it caught fire—that old heavy oil was hard to burn,
and they had some men around. Now, I know one boy—I can't recall his name now—well, he was throwing dirt in there when a spark
set this other tank to put it out, but something they didn't realize—
this oil burned down, but the fire got right down there close to that
water—that water got hot enough to boil. Well, here she comes,
right out of there, clear across the prairie, and he saw that start, and
he said he run for a half a mile, and he said he thought that fire was
right behind him. Well, it did catch—I expect, several of them—
burnt up some teams and everything in its path.

One of the funniest things about that, they run an excursion
out of Galveston and Houston, and this fire created a big rain in the
state around there and rained right down through there. It was raining soot and ink. A bunch of ladies come out there and got in a hack
to go out to see the fire, and the hack broke down, and they had
to wade back through that mud and that ink raining down on them.
Some of them came up. I was up at the depot when they came in.
I had seen all the fires I wanted before that. When they got in there,

some of them had their shoes in their hands, and if they weren't the awfulest-looking, drab bunch. They just as black as if they had been dipped in ink, all horrible.

—*Hardeman Roberts*

They had another fire right near, on Moonshine Hill, right near the boardinghouse where I was sitting eating breakfast at eight one morning. Lightning hit one of these Guffey tanks, and jumped from that down to two five-hundred-barrel tanks probably a quarter of a mile away. Tanks belonged to Howard Hughes.

I was watching the tanks when the lightning struck. Of course, they blew up and burned all day. When they boiled over, and over the fire wall, flaming oil flowed down through draws or ravines and surrounded an air-compressor plant of J. H. McEvoy's, that had been running up to the very last, and we shut down, figuring that the fire would get him.

But by evening it was still there. Fire had escaped him by going down these ravines, one on each side, and the boardinghouse where I stayed, where I was eating breakfast when it struck, escaped also. The landlady had left with all her clothing and gone over to Moonshine Hill and stayed, and told us we could come back at noon and get our food ourself if the place was still there. And we did, and that night we returned there and stayed because it was safe. The fire was still burning, but it was no danger to anybody at that time.

—*Early C. Deane*

The terrible fire we had there was in the fall after it started raining so much there. It was in 1919. And it was this fifty-five-thousand-barrel tank set right up on a knoll and right in the edge of this little old shack town, everybody called it.

That was New Town. And, this electric storm that afternoon, lightning struck that tank and just burst it wide open. That oil, just solid flame, spread out on that water, just enveloped those houses and drilling rigs and shacks of all kinds, clear down to Main Street and into this creek, burnt up so many people before they ever knew that there was a fire. Everybody was indoors that could get indoors from the rain and nobody realized that this lightning had struck this tank until they were just surrounded by flames, and there is no telling—nobody ever knew, I don't suppose—how many people burnt up, but I would say there was around four hundred or five hundred.

Women and children was screaming; I never heard such a thing in my life. You know it was just terrible. People just running and them afire and just running and screaming and hollering and there was no place to go; it was all around them. It was about the worst disaster I guess that—well, a man could imagine happening in a town like that. It hit right in the center of the thickest populated parts and it burnt up all the stores and those little old clothing stores and stuff were all just built in shacks, burnt up those. It just practically wiped the town out.

They come in there with those trucks. They'd just couple those big old Nash quad trucks together with chains, load them with nurses and doctors and clothing and bedding and everything they could get and just came in there. They set up a big tent over there on the hillside, kind of temporary quarters, and they got all the people that were burnt that they could care for in that tent. Some of them they took to Wichita Falls and some of them other places where they were capable of being hauled further. They took them just anywhere they could get them to give them medical aid and got all the doctors and nurses possible to help with it.

—*Jack Knight*

Storage-tank Explosions

In these cypress tanks they'd put in about, about a yard from the top, a false bottom, and fill in with dirt on top. Below this false bottom they'd put in a bent pipe for the gas to escape while it was flowing in this tank. They had had some experience with that bad gas, so they ordered everybody to put in a jet, a steam jet in the mouth of this pipe, so that when you changed a well to the other tank, if there wasn't sufficient gas to carry the flames far away, this steam jet would put it out, or the fire would follow back to the pipe and explode the tank.

It was a common agreement amongst everybody. But Mr. Trammell apparently was in such a hurry to get out his oil he didn't follow the regulation of putting in this steam jet, but he had to set his gas flare. It was such a vehement gas it would have poisoned everybody in the fields.

He lit the gas flare all right. Something went wrong with the well one day, probably clogged up through some more of this gum ball that we had blowed out of the well with the compressed air, and it stopped flowing. When it did, the gas followed back, and exploded the tank and burned up everything in that edge of the field.

About that same time, there was another well, about, I'd say, two hundred yards from there. I heard an explosion one day and the rattling of tubing, and looked in time to see the tubing moving in the top of the derrick, three triple joints. Well, that explosion was in a flow tank also, of green cypress lumber; the gauger had been on this tank, and what caused the explosion nobody ever knew. But from the explosion, it set this waste afire, which it was finally put out by chemical extinguishers. The gauger was killed.

—W. M. Hudson, Sr.

Fire at Batson

I don't know the number of the well, but it was in a flat there [at Batson]. They finally fought it out with steam and stuff. As far as I remember the well was leaking, got sort of loose some way around the casing. In them days they wasn't using casing heads; didn't hardly know what they was. The separators they used in them days was made out of the tanks. About two, three feet from the top they'd put in a false top and then pump that full of mud and top it over. They didn't put any checks [check valves, which permit the fluid to flow in only one direction] on them lines and whenever they'd switch from one tank to another, pull that fire right back through there and blow that thing up.

That's what started that fire in that flat there, you see. That's the first or second time I ever wore a helmet, was in there, putting that bradenhead—they called them in them days—on, the casing head on that well. You had to use them or the gas'd kill you. You couldn't stand it. That's about all there was to that fire. It lasted ten or twelve days, something like that. They soon get shed of the fire after that oil burnt off, you see, and flooded that with water and pushed that oil on away. They could blow it out with steam.

—Sam W. Webb

Lots of Destruction

One of the worst fires that I experienced was down in the heart of the oil field. It was a tremendous fire, and it burnt up lots of wells, equipment, tanks, and storage and done a great deal of destruction. Now, another fire was in the west end, the Christian Oil Company. I suppose there was at least sixty acres of oil that burnt to the ground, and it happened about noon, and that was sometime in the year of 1906. And it just leveled everything before it. And, of course, there was numerous other fires, not as great; however, done lots of destruction, but I mention them two as about the largest.

—*James Donohoe*

The Death of Pat Connally

We was over at Humble. We was out in the field and that time we set separators. This separator was made out of steel just like a big drum, but instead of setting it upright like they do today, we laid it down on the ground.

And we come out there with a six-inch nipple and a six-inch ell, then a long nipple about six foot long, and dug big pits. And we dropped this ell on the end and put another piece of pipe down for the suction [to] lift the oil out, because at that time they had no way of getting rid of this gas—they were afraid to burn it. Just pick up the pumps and pump it into the tank. We didn't have any steel tanks. The only steel tanks was then the storage tanks of these big corporations, the pipe-line companies. What we had was cypress and redwood tanks, maybe sixteen-hundred- to two-fifty-hundred-barrel tanks, anything we could get ahold of.

Well, we had to pick two up, and in the meantime when we were putting this separator in, it seems like a coupling on this ell was left loose, and the gas was going up in the air. The wells were close together. Our well had just come in, and we had three boilers setting out there furnishing steam for the drilling rig. This drilling rig had brought the well in. The ell was loose on the nipple going into the separator, and it just lifted up, and the well was gone before they could shut it off. Shot a six-inch stream of oil on the three boilers.

Mr. Connally was standing there watching the well, so he saw it and hollered to me, "Frank, you're going to burn up everything, going to catch everything afire." And he run in there to cut this gas off on all three boilers—one valve would have closed all three of them off. We had this main valve back on the two-inch line. He bent over to cut them off and about that time, why, it ignited and caught him there. He was burned beyond—well, you couldn't even recognize him. Still we looked for him after the fire was out. After we turned the steam in on the fire to blow the fire out, we looked for him, and we found him under a tree, where he had crawled with no feet. Didn't have any feet on him. Nothing but bones.

I got out there, and he asked for a drink of water. Some of the boys said, "Don't give it to him because it's liable to kill him." Another boy spoke up—Johnny—he was a driller—said, "Well, just as well give it to him, because he is going to die anyhow." Just black flesh had fallen off awful. He didn't last long. We couldn't hardly pick him up—we didn't have automobiles then. Anyhow, we picked him up in a wagon. Had quilts and a mattress in there—just wrapped him up in a sheet. He was already dead by the time we started. He was gasping when he wanted that drink of water—he was gasping then. I guess he must have inhaled that flame down in his lungs. He died a terrible death. Well, in those days we had no safety. There wasn't nothing else. There wasn't nothing safe.

—*Frank Hamilton*

The Death of the Teamsters

The worst fire I ever saw in a field was in Humble. It was a Texas Company tank—lightin' hit 'em and they had, I believe it was, four tanks and one caught on fire. Well, they taken a number of teams and men and went in there and was cutting a ditch between this particular tank that was on fire and the others. They knew it would finally boil over, but they thought they would cut the channel before it did. But the tank boiled over and caught those men and teams in there.

I went out after the fire died down and I think it burnt for seven days before we got in there and help pick up the men, and they was mules and scrapers all over the tank farm and I believe we picked up seventeen men and some of them—of course we didn't know whether they was niggers or whites—they was charred—there wasn't anything but the trunk of the body. We turned the mules over—maybe the mules had fell on a man—and we could tell whether he was white—but the only way they ever knew how many men was lost was from the Texas Company payroll, from the books. That was the worst fire I ever saw.

—*W. H. (Bill) Bryant*

Three or Four Within an Hour

We've seen many of those places [at Spindletop] blow out. We saw many, many wells blow out, come in and just absolutely obliterate the surface, and blow a hole in the ground twice as big as the platform that the derrick was setting on, and just make a mud pie out of it. It'd blow those casings, and also the drill stems, blow them into the air and they'd break into pieces, two and three and four joints apiece, and then fall back and a whole joint would stick into the ground all the way, halfway up, and break off and bend. We saw many, many of those happen.

You know when a well was going to come in or break, it would blow the foundation off of the well where the equipment was and the derrick man would be up there and he would have to swing down on the guy wire from the well in order to keep from being destroyed. We saw many of those, just actually saw them, every detail of that. If a man was up there, he couldn't come down on the walls of that derrick, because the mud and stuff that come out of the top of that casing as a rule would scatter like that, you see, up through the derrick. He'd pull his clothes off and slide down those wires to keep this wire from cutting his hands in two. And many of them got away that way. Some lost their lives, of course, due to the fact that they were blown loose from the building and blown loose from anything that they might be holding onto. Many of them lost their lives that way. It's hard to tell how many accidents happened of that kind because sometimes there would be three or four within an hour and maybe you'd only see two. Maybe you'd only hear about one.

—H. C. Sloop

He Never Stopped to Pull His Apron Off

The war in Europe started. England declared war on Germany, or France and England. And George Kennedy was peculiar on it, and he was putting up most of the money. And he called everything off. He said he wouldn't spend any more money with a war going on. Afraid he'd lose his money or he didn't like war. I don't know exactly what his reason was.

Well, my crewmen and myself of course went into town. Always had a room at the hotel. The Pavilion Hotel was Walker's hotel. And some of my crew also stayed there. We became tired of loafing, and along in November—no I'd say October [1914]—I went to Kennedy and Walker and told them if they would stake me, that I would try to finish the well. They said all right.

Our transportation was sailboats from Corpus Christi across the Bay, which was eight miles. We had a Mexican sailor to do our transporting. We were drilling on what was known as the Rachelle Ranch, nineteen hundred acres. The Rachelles were old-timers, old ranchers in that country, and mighty fine people. Well, I went over and took my crew and we repaired the boiler, put in some new flues, one thing and another, and got started. I drilled on down till somewhere about twenty-one hundred and fifty feet, something like that. The gas began to show up very strong. Very fortunate I had lots of heavy mud in the bay that I could very easily pump into the well, and mud will hold gas back for a length of time. I urged them though to try to prepare the well for an eventual blowout. They said, "Oh, let her blow. That's what I want."

Walker came over from the hotel to help me, working just as one of the roustabouts. I had pulled the pipe from the well the night before and was replacing it in the well the next morning, that was November twelfth. And about ten o'clock the well made a few belches and, my God, all at once here came the pipe roaring through, up, up, up. Knocked the crown block over, split the derrick, hung my traveling block way up almost to the top of the derrick. And here came the mud gushing.

That pipe went through and came over the derrick on one side. Some of it corkscrewed. And seven hundred fifty feet of it made a complete somersault and fell lengthwise down the edge of the bay. In the meantime Walker had made a run and not having his shoe laced, stepped out of his shoe—it was a little muddy—and the pipe fell across his shoe, a narrow escape. Of course we all got away. My old Norwegian cook, who was in what we called a cook shack, just a hundred yards or so away from the well, he never stopped to pull his apron off. He just went right on through the brush. I stayed till I seen it was unnecessary to stay any longer. And I moved out, too, and dodged some of that falling pipe.

Well, it blew for days, and they could hear it in Corpus Christi. It rattled the windows, kept the people awake at night. And I believe it was the third or fourth day it began to blow the casing. We had about, I guess, fifteen hundred feet of casing, eight-inch I believe it was. And it began to whip, just unwind this casing and break it off. It would go so high that a length of eight-inch casing would look like a cigar, and come down and stick in the ground. And all we could do was watch it.

After blowing that casing, all of it to the top, the soft earth became loose and caved in. And the other casing dropped down and shut off the water. Then it went to whistling dry gas. They could hear that loud screaming whistling as far down as Rockport, that was twenty-five miles away. And many people came up the bay to see what was wrong, from Rockport and Aransas Pass. Well, they soon found out. My Mexican that was my boatman happened to be there that morning. He made a run and he didn't get back for two days.

Day or so after the gusher of mud ceased, the whole earth around the well caved in. Next morning there was nothing but a seething cavern of mud. Sometimes it would gather head and be blown for a hundred feet in the air. I counted thirteen live geysers, out in the Bay a hundred or so yards, shooting all at one time, some of them as much as a hundred feet high, seemingly so.

Eventually I had the boys get out and cut a gap and let some of the water go into the Bay; that they did. We only salvaged the engine to the rig and saved the tool house by getting some mules from the Rachelle Ranch hurriedly and dragged them away. And also managed to drag the boiler away. All of the rest went into the hole, swallowed up all the rest of the rig. It's still in there, nobody knows how deep.

—W. D. Bowen

Swabbing a Well

Well, swabbing a well in the early days of Humble consisted of tying a gunny sack around the top of your bailer and letting it down slowly through the fluid and then pulling it up more quickly, or as quickly as you could, with the old horse we had in those days, and pulling a jag of oil out ahead of it. Well, the sulphur gas was terrifically poisonous. Finally got to where we paid gas time and hospitalization for men.

I was swabbing this well which Lee Blaffer and Bill Farish owned, and I'd let this bailer down and the wind was blowing back toward where the driller had to stand, and I'd kick the clutch in, then I had me a little piece of rubber hose that I'd throw over the brake and the clutch and I'd walk back behind the engine where I could get to the throttle to shut it off in case anything went wrong, and let this sulphur gas blow where the driller was supposed to be and I was not. Well, Mr. Farish didn't think much of the idea, and he was a big, husky fellow and he got a little impatient at my apparent delaying tactics. "Oh," he said, "I know how to run that thing. I'll just bail it."

I said, "Mr. Farish, that sulphur'll knock you out. It'll knock anybody out."

"Oh, it won't knock me out."

So he goes in and starts swabbing. And you could see this gas roll out, you know, and this little old soft breeze just a-blowing it right down his throat. And he stood it for quite a little while, and he started up with another jag and his knees begun to buckle like a fellow who's taken a haymaker in a prize fight. I ran over to the engine and shut it off right where it was and started in on the derrick floor. Well, of course, in the swabbing, we had swabbed out some bad muddy water and it was an inch or two thick on the derrick floor and when my old friend William fell, he fell smack on his face with his nose right in that stuff.

If ever you saw an ordinary well digger wrestling with a big load of human being, you should have seen me trying to get Brother Farish off of that thing and out into a pine thicket where I could ride him a little bit and pump some of that stuff out of him. I got a little assist from two or three of the boys that worked on the rig. They'd gotten well out of the range of this gas and they ran over and we dragged him over and turned him and give him a little first aid and jumped up and down on that big set of lungs he had and knocked some air in him.

Well, he never did forget that. The last time I saw him was during the centennial planning at Dallas. They had a big party there, and he was then chairman of the board of the Standard of New Jersey. He was the honored guest and the chief speaker, and he saw me in the hotel lobby. And he went very promptly over to the arrangement committee and he said, "Now, I see my old friend Walter Cline's here, and I want him to sit by me tonight. I want him to talk to me." Well, it wasn't according to the schedule at all and they tried as tactfully as they could to explain that they had some heavyweights that were supposed to sit up there around the throne, and he said, "I don't give a damn what you got. I'm the honored guest and I'm gonna make this speech, and I'm gonna sit by Walter Cline. Now, if you want me to sit up there, make room for him. If you don't, I'll sit down at the table where he sits." So I sat by Bill and he again referred to this swabbing incident.

—*Walter Cline*

I Didn't Figure I Had No Business There

The discovery well in the Fitts field was down on the Harding lease. Jack Shaffer drilled it and Jack Shaffer was a drilling contractor. I was down there and we looked after the drilling of that well. That well cratered. Cratered out and left quite a hole.

My wife and I, we was down there, we was at a little old pump station out there, but the field was originally supposed to be to the north of this field, and we had this water station down there and we was getting water up there at a well, up there by old man Harding's house. Well, we was up there that night and she stood there at the well and I walked across a log across the creek and went over there to see how it was getting along.

I was standing there and I heard something go *s-s-s-s-s-s-t* in the ground, and it was a crawfish hole and this gas and mud just come up out of that crawfish hole. And about that time, I started to go back across there, see, because I didn't figure I had no business around there, and when I got over there just a little ways, here come another one. I went right on across this log, see, across the creek, and my wife and I was standing there and, boy, it was getting bigger and bigger and bigger and directly it just blowed. I mean blowed it out, right out. Blowed it out just dry as a chip.

—*C. W. Bland*

Unsuccessful By-pass

While we were working those wells [in Tampico, Mexico] and I was flowing it, one morning I heard a terrific explosion and saw the tubing which was standing up in the derrick, about two hundred yards away, falling from one side of the derrick to the other. Everybody in the field was making tracks to get there to see what had happened. When I arrived, when I got within fifty yards of the derrick, I found a Mexican helper with a hole in one side of his head, and part of his brains showing; a little farther on, another one badly wounded. And when I got to the well, I was informed that there was three men that went into the pit, to try to change the pressure off of the lower valve, which was stuck on account of having nine hundred pounds pressure to the square inch, and apparently they were trying to make a by-pass, to take the pressure off this lower valve.

Well, seems like one of the Mexican helpers took a wrench and caught hold of some nut, or some bolt, or clamp, or something, and anyway he made a slight move with the wrench and that caused the explosion on account of the high pressure, and they were both seriously injured; at that time, they took the American driller out with a hole in his back the size of your fist and he died within a few minutes.

—W. M. Hudson, Sr.

Safety: Old and New

The promotion of safety is one of the greatest improvements I think they have made. The safety campaign we've had made the people safety-conscious. Then, when they are injured severely or lose an arm or leg, better care that they take of them. It used to be you just drew arrears. If you lost your leg or arm or hand, why, that was just your own hard luck; you shouldn't have done it. You should have been more careful. And you were thrown into discard; got along the best way you could. That is one of the greatest improvements we have made, is in safety.

Our fire improvement has been wonderful. In the old days we had no conservation program, and a new oil field would come in, it would be produced just to the limit, just as fast as it could, and just as much as it could, and they would build these big tanks to hold the oil. Then we had no efficient way of protecting them from lightning. Lightning would frequently hit them, then they would burn sometimes for days and around these large tank farms that they used to have, I've seen tank farms with hundreds of tanks in them. One of the standard equipment was a cannon that would shoot a hole in the side of the tank down close to the bottom and let the oil out in a dike.

If the tank was pretty well full after it started burning there would be a certain number of hours that this oil underneath the fire would become so heated that it would boil over, and I've seen flames go as much as two or three miles in the air from this. In boiling over like this, it would very often ignite tanks close to it, so that is one of the reasons that they liked to shoot into the side of the tank with the cannon and let the oil out in the dike and let it start burning at a low even rate of burning.

The first oil fire I ever saw was two tanks burned at Bridgeport, Illinois, in the late summer of 1907. And seems to me that all the old-timers kind of date from that fire of those two tanks. "Did you go to Bridgeport before those tanks burnt or after?" That was kind of a dating there, and we knew then nothing about the tanks boiling over.

I can remember watching them from a distance when they started to boil over, and I started to run as everyone else did, looking back over my shoulder, and seeing that fire; seems to me it was miles high, and that was a greater impression of the hereafter to me than any sermon I had ever heard. Made me think of the hereafter, if there was going to be anything like that I most certainly didn't want to go to it.

—O. J. *Lawson*

The type men forty years ago—either roughnecks or derrick men or drillers on a rotary rig or tool dressers and drillers on string cable tools—were somewhat different from the type men you have now. First of all, the tool joint had not been patented. There was no Wilson or any other kind of crank tongs. The only way we could break out a joint of pipe was with two sets of Vulcan tongs or cleats nailed on the floor and put about two men on each side opposite of each other and pull. And if some sand had gotten into the joint and had stripped the threads off, we laid down two joints and tried another one. And if we bent the pipe to where we thought it was unsafe, why, we laid it down.

The cathead was not used for any purpose, breaking, or setting, or anything else. And there were no safety devices at all. We drove the rotary with a cast-iron chain that would break at the slightest provocation and if you were standing anywhere within six or eight foot in front of it, it would wrap around your leg or your belly or your neck, flop you around a little bit. It was usually sufficiently greasy and short that nobody to my knowledge was ever killed.

There was no guards, nor guides, nor nobody that knew anything about steel helmets, brass-toed shoes; and nobody bothered to turn over a board if it had a nail sticking up in it, or pick up a loose piece of pipe to keep the people from stepping on it. There just was no thought given to the personal safety and no safety devices, and the men who were in the oil business had to be big and they had to be tough. And they had to do work.

A little fellow now can run a rig and do the heaviest part of the work because they've learned to let the machinery do the lifting and do the pulling and do the work. And we used to do it with man-power, and the men, being big and rugged and hard, lived pretty hard. They drank more than you'll find the average boy drinking now.

—Walter Cline

KNOW-
HOW

10

Until the age of electronics, high-precision instruments and computers, the basic tools and techniques for the production of oil were devised by the men on the job. The standard rig was in its essential principle as old as civilization and had been used in ancient China. The chief innovations of the Americans who adapted it to salt-water drilling were the substitution of steam power for human muscle and cable for bamboo poles, and the development of various accessories, such as the rope socket, the temper screw (for letting out cable as needed), jars (sliding links to allow play or "jar" as the drill stem was raised and lowered), fishing tools (for recovering objects lost in the well), and many others. These uncomplicated devices could be made by any competent blacksmith. Many parts of the rig, including the walking beam, the Samson post, and the bull wheels, were made of wood, and could be fashioned by any millwright or wheelwright.

The salt drillers became oil drillers and passed their skills on to their helpers, called tool dressers (they sharpened the bits), or toolies. The opening of vast new fields at the beginning of this century brought many of these workers to the Southwest, but not enough to man the rigs. Local men, however, quickly developed the necessary skills. Initially there was some friction between the outsiders and the natives. The Texans and the Oklahomans thought that the Pennsylvanians and West Virginians were too cautious, too set in their ways, and called them mossbacks. The veterans assumed that the recruits knew little or nothing, and they were inclined to be patronizing if not a bit hostile. But the natives proved their adaptability. They were not, as operators abroad found the Latin Americans, the Burmese, and the Indians to be, unfamiliar with the simple principles of mechanics.

Although the region was relatively unindustrialized when the Lucas Gusher blew in, railroad shops, sawmills, cotton gins, and cottonseed-processing plants operating in many towns and villages gave employment and imparted skills to many young men from the farm. And although the farms were not yet motorized, mechanization was well under way. The farm boys had had experience with seeders, mowing machines, reapers, binders, and threshing machines and knew how to operate and maintain them. They approached the drilling rig with confidence.

In the use of rotary equipment they had the advantage, for the rotary process had not been used in the older oil states. By the late '90s, Corsicana had turned out a goodly number of competent rotary drillers. And in the days of Spindletop, Batson, Sour Lake, and Saratoga, it was said that any man from Corsicana could get a job as driller whether he had ever worked on a rig or not.

As the industry developed, machine shops multiplied, and the mechanics had the skill and the equipment to fashion the devices that workers and their supervisors designed to meet their regular and emergency needs. And many needs had to be met locally, for manufacturers did not anticipate them. Nor was there a corps of scientifically trained men to turn to. It was not until 1910 that the United States Bureau of Mines was established and the University of Pittsburgh became the first to offer courses in petroleum engineering: three courses in oil and gas and three in petroleum law. In 1914, Stanford University offered a course in the technology of petroleum. In 1931, the University of Texas graduated a class of two in petroleum engineering. By 1965, twenty-seven universities in fifteen states were offering graduate or undergraduate degrees in the field.

But the knowledge and skill of these men were not generally available to the industry until the '30s and '40s. In the meantime, the operators and their drillers and roughnecks and those associated with them met their problems as best they could. In getting the oil out of the ground they were remarkably successful. They lacked the knowledge and the sophisticated instruments to get it out with the maximum recovery. They did not lack incentive. From the beginning, a man could work his way up—from toolie to driller, from boll weevil to pusher, to owning a rig, a well, a producing field.

Inventions Just Happened

Inventions then, they just kind of happened so. If you'd need a tool, you'd think about it, you'd rig it up and go to the machine shop and have it made. Never think anything about getting a patent on it. Such things as the overshot, go in the shop and have them made, and spears of various kinds. Never thought about getting a patent on them, you see. In each individual fishing job, even at this date, you'll get a problem sometimes that you can't find a tool that you think will just fit, and you'll have to go and make it just a little different maybe from something you had to use or tried to use on that particular job.

The man who thought of the idea seldom got credit for it. I think very seldom. The average driller or contractor would go get what he'd need, rush out and use it and maybe throw it in the corner of his derrick or tool house and not think much about it. Of course, patents to us in those days didn't seem to amount to anything much.

—*Al Hamill*

It seems to me the typical American boy every time he goes to do anything he starts doing it different, trying to find a better and a faster way and easier way of doing it. And he has that insatiable curiosity that I think that has made America what it has. What it is.

—*O. G. Lawson*

Learning How

When they was running those rocks, why, they had lots of time. They'd sit around and shoot the bull, just ordinary conversations. Their principal conversation was the current events or the local happening. They wasn't paying no attention—oh, except the boy that might be interested in advancing, why, he would watch the operation of the machinery and learn how to handle it and try to learn how to set it up, take it down and move. Some of them read the formation in a bucket as it come out of the ground. There was quite a few old-timers that came from West Virginia and Pennsylvania that were exceptionally good looking at those cuttings in that mud bucket and telling you what it was and where it was at. There was any number of them that were gifted with the ability to take that mud up there and run that sand through their fingers, and some of them could tell you what it would do and what it wouldn't do.

That's what made a driller, was his ability to read his mud. They washed it, see. They didn't have the modern shaker that they got now and the chemicals and methods. To test it, they would put it in clear water and wash it. Put it in a fruit jar, take a stick and stir it up. Then a druggist hit upon the bright idea of using chloroform. And they could take those porous rocks that the bit would knock loose and put them in a bowl and chloroform them. And that's where they discovered that the oil was in the rock.

—*Plummer M. Barfield*

The Rotary Drill

The factory at Corsicana is what is known as the Bethlehem Steel now. It grew from a blacksmith shop to a machine shop and then a steady growth through the years. It covers approximately three blocks now, city blocks. In the early days Johnston, Akin, and Rittersbacher was the founders of that shop. Of course, all of those people are dead now, but they started out with a blacksmith shop, dressing these bits, you know, for rigs around here, and they had them a cable-tool rig theirself.

They manufactured cable tools. And then they manufactured the rotary rig there. This fellow Baker, that invented that rotary, he sold the rights to Johnston and Akin but drew royalty on those rotaries. Every rotary rig that was put out, Baker got twelve-fifty on that rotary.

And after he died—why, his nephew still drew that royalty, and they still draw it today; as far as I know he's still drawing it. The patent covered the rotary, not the draw works. [M. C. and C. E. Baker are credited with the development of the first operational rotary in Dakota Territory about 1883. They used parts of farm machines in making their working model.]

                                                        —M. A. Johnson

Drilling with Mud

I wish to give my full version of the making of a pit of mud that was made and used during the month of December 1900, on what was called the Lucas well and was the discovery well at Spindletop, near Beaumont, Texas.

About three days prior to making the mud we encountered a coarse water sand that gave us lots of trouble. We had pulled three or four plug bits. When the bit was taken off the pipe, there would be two or six feet of sand in the pipe. We had just pulled a plug bit when the wood wagon drove up with a few pine slabs. He said that was all the slabs that was at the railroad switch. The car of slabs expected had not been placed. Al, the contractor, said we would not go back in the hole until some wood could be had.

As soon as Al had gone, we told the wood hauler to go to his headquarters, which was Reverend Chaney's home and corral, and have him send teams and equipment to clean the slush pit. It was about two o'clock when the teams arrived at the well. They had six mules, four colored men, and a white man who rode a pony. They had a heavy walking plow and a Fresno scraper on the wagon, also some chain and a wire cable about forty feet long.

It was almost sundown. The men were through [cleaning the pit] and fixing to leave. Reverend Chaney rode up on a pony. He wanted to know why so much sand. We told him of the sand strata that we had. We told him if we could get some heavy, muddy water it might help us. He said he could make us all the muddy water we wanted. Our contractor, Al, was not there, so Peck Byrd and myself decided to have the mud made.

The teams arrived at the well early in the morning, having the same equipment that was used in cleaning the pit the day before. This time a plow was used. The bottom of the pit was clay. They plowed it shallow, then deeper, and then deeper until the plow had gone down at least ten inches. Then we started to pump water from the bayou into the pit.

At this time, Mr. John [Chaney], as the darkies called him, left on his pony for the cows. The cows had been driven to a gate in a small pasture some four hundred or five hundred yards away. In a short time, Mr. John came back riding in front of the cows. Two colored men on horseback were driving the cows. The mules had been tied to the derrick and were turned enough so Mr. John rode through the pit leading the cattle. When he got through the pit, the mules were tied back to the derrick, closing the trap that had been planned, excepting the entrance. One pony was tied to the derrick and one to the iron wheel of the wagon. Mr. John tied his pony to the horn of the saddle of one pony, but these ponies, two men, kept the cows in the pit. About twelve inches of water was in the pit at this time.

It was no small job getting the cows in the pit. Some of the herd got away, but there was plenty put in the pit to do the job. The cows were allowed some time to get settled before they were made to move around. A man stood on each ledge. He would poke the cows on the back with a long whip that was used to drive four or six mules in those days. The cows were left in the pit about four hours. Water was being pumped in the pit all the time. The cows did a good job as we found the plowed place to be a muck when we got back to work.

Al arrived at the well about three o'clock that evening. We were circulating muddy water. Peck was firing the boiler and watching the pump. I was holding the one-inch joint of pipe. Al wanted to know what we were doing. Peck told him. Al said, "That will do no good." Peck told him the machinery work had all been done and we were ready to go drilling any time. Al said that there would be plenty of wood here by night to start drilling in the morning. He had secured dry cork, wood, several wagonloads of pine knots, and a car of slabs that had been sent at the railroad switch.

All of this was delivered on time and we had no more shortages. We put the new jet in the water well and it did fine. The discharge was three quarters of an inch. We talked Al into filling the boiler pit first as the water was low in it. Peck brought in a four-inch collar from the buckboard that had been made into a drill bit by putting a steel blade across in a slot with a rod through the blade and both sides of the collar, and ribbed it at both ends. Al said he would use that collar for our drill bit as it would not get plugged with sand.

We started in the hole with the drill bit and got to the bottom of the eight-inch casing by quitting time. Al was much sold on his new drill collar, the blade. Peck and myself were sold on the mud idea. That night we talked over what and how it had been done and Chaney had advanced the idea, and, Al not being there, we had mud made.

The following morning, Al decided not to put any more water in the slush pit until we had found if the mud was of value so we went to circulating water as before and did this until the water was red and thick. We finished going in the hole. When we reached the sand, we lost almost half of our muddy water. The heavier mud carried a quantity of roots and chunks of mud that gave us lots of trouble. The foot valves were taken off the pumps' suctions and the heavy mud was rigged to the suction and went through the pump into the well. We had lots of pump trouble but got through the strata of sand that day and into gumbo.

Peck ran the pump until midnight that night and Al went out at midnight and ran the pump until that morning. This was done until we had gotten through all of our trouble. He had made about four feet of hole in the gumbo and had not lost any more water when Peck and myself got back on the job with him. Al said he could not make any headway with the blade so we pulled it and ran a fishtail bit. The bit went to the bottom of the hole, which was gumbo. It made some mud and we had no more sand trouble. Six-inch pipe was set on the twenty-fourth day of December without any trouble. Did this bit of mud save the Lucas well?

After the gusher came in, Jim Sharp learned about the mud

and made the first mud mixer that was made on the Spindletop field which was proved to be a success, and almost every drilling rig in the field had a mud mixer patterned after the Sharp machine. Mr. Sharp told me after looking at his mud machine that if it hadn't been for Peck and myself and Reverend Chaney making the mud with the cattle, he would not have thought of making this mud mixer.

—Curt G. Hamill

Trouble with the Drilling Mud

Well, I was roughnecking when I first went there, roughnecking for my brother-in-law. The way I started, the American Well and Prospecting Company sold the Blanchard Oil Company a drilling rig, and they wanted my brother-in-law to run this rig for them and they wanted me to be the night driller. So I did, and that's where I started drilling. I guess we made the first well in the old Caddo field that'd ever been made without a blowout. One reason we did it, I sat up with it at night; I didn't go to sleep on the job. I sat up with that old well. I was afraid for it to blow out, and I stayed with it. Lots of times it'd try to blow out. I never will forget once it was trying to blow out and every once in a while it'd squirt the mud and the oil clean up over the rotary, you know, old thick, heavy mud. And I'd have the boys out mixing mud and letting more mud in the slush pit all the time. It was gurgling a way down in the hole —I could hear it. Went and stuck my head over the rotary to look down in there, and just about that time it gushed up and that mud just went all over me, all in my eyes and everywhere, you know. Well, anyway, we made that well.

We couldn't let the mud git thin. If we did it'd blow out right quick. It rained, while I was on that well; it rained thirty nights, just straight, all night long it rained. And every morning about daylight it began to clear up. Wouldn't rain a bit all day, and that night about the time we'd start work, it'd start raining again. And it rained all night long.

We had trouble keeping that mud thick enough, you know. Had trouble; we had to dig reserve pits there to keep mud stored in, to hold it. And we had trouble keeping the dams from washing away on this reserve pit. I remedied that, though. We had a bunch of big eight- and ten-inch nipples there, about six or eight feet long, and I took them and buried them down in the top of that reserve pit levee all the way around, one every few feet, and let the end of them, top end of them, stick right up level with the top of the mud, you know. Before I did that, had to keep somebody walking around and around that slush pit all night to keep the mud from washing away. After I did that, didn't have no trouble. Them pipes would just keep the water cleaned off the top and leave the mud in there, you know, and didn't have no more trouble losing the mud.

—J. T. (Cotton) Young

Putting Out a Fire with Explosives

Another fire I saw, let's see, that was over in Texas, right on the Louisiana line. This man was named C. M. Chester. I guess there was a lot of men know him, because he was a general superintendent of the Texas Company. This well was afire and shooting straight up. Derrick was all gone, so he went ahead and he figured out that he could take a basket full of dynamite and time him a fuse and swing this on a cable, you see. Built the stuff out there to hold the cable, you see, and could swing this and time it so that about the time it hit over the top of the flame it would go off. And that jar would put it out. The flame, I imagine, was going about one hundred and seventy-five foot in the air. Well, he took one stick and timed these fuses. And he swung it over there and when it went off, it jarred that flame out.

That was the first one I ever knew that was put out by explosion. I don't remember what year that was, but I think it was about 1908. I think that's about the time. C. M. Chester was the first man I ever heard of that figured out that steel basket and slugging it over.

—Frank Hamilton

The Roller Rock Bit

I was very well acquainted with the man that first got up the roller bit, the Hughes roller bit, old man Johnny Wynn, now down here on College Street running a little shop, sharpening saws and mowers and one thing and another. He got up that crude roller bit, known as the Hughes bit now. And Mr. Hughes, I understood, gave him fifteen hundred dollars for his patent. That's how [Howard] Hughes started. Mr. Wynn now, I expect he's up toward ninety years old. You could talk to him. He's the first rotary driller that I ever knew. I was about eleven years old when I met him. He drilled a water well for a little town, Arlington, up close to Fort Worth.

He came in there with a crude outfit, little pressure engine boiler, small pumps, fought seven or eight months there before he ever got down and made a water well, but they made a water well and I think the water well is still getting water, producing water up there at Arlington now. I was about eleven years old at that time. My father run a blacksmith shop there at Arlington. He did the bit sharpening. You might say it was more of an experiment, anyway, when they first got them out.

—*Claude Deer*

After I drilled the Sour Lake Oil Company's well, being no supplies or any shop anywheres nearer than Beaumont, I went in the supply business and I oiled machinery, did repairing, worked over the machines in my shop, the J. S. Wynn Machine Shop.

The idea came to me very simple. I was sitting by a big lathe on some castings, and on the floor was an eight-inch pipe setter which we used to set our pipe in the earth, so I got to spinning that setter around on the floor, just passing time, and discovered that it turned in a circle, an eight-inch circle. So it came to me why I couldn't place those cones on a body to be attached at a drill stem to drill rock in the hole in the ground. So it came to me like I give. Don't know why, but just from that playing with that cone.

Ever since I had been working in the well business, we all talked and wanted some idea on how to drill rock. The fishtail would only just grind and wear at it, and we'd use adamantine and other stuff to core and set rock, but that was all a slow process. And we'd want to know why we couldn't make a drill that would go through rock and that was my idea in putting these cones on the body, to drill rock.

I made my first model in 1908, I think it was. I made it at Sour Lake, and got my draftsman, Denison, and our lawyer to get the patent for me. The model, a working model, I used in the shop drilling through marble slabs and rock and things. That bit lay around in Sour Lake shop there and we would look at it, you know, and talk. And when I closed my Sour Lake shop, I moved her over to Batson and had it in my Batson shop, and it stayed there quite a while. I could see it didn't have clearance to cleanse that earth from the body, so I'd studied different ways but hadn't put it in effect.

So Monahan, foreman for the Sun Company, drilled over at Bazette, and struck this rock. Couldn't drill it with the rotary. So they first welded a pair of cable tools to drill through. They found some oil showing, and they wanted to drill further. They drilled a second hole down to this rock and Monahan had seen the drill at the shop. He says, "Why not let me take this drill out yonder and see what it'll do? I'd like to try it." And I says, "All right. You can go ahead and do it."

So he taken it out with him and when they was putting it on the drill stem to drill, the driller says, "Oh, there ain't no use putting this thing on. It ain't gonna make no hole." Monahan says, "Not costing us anything." Says, "We can go ahead and try it."

So they put it in the hole and got down on bottom, commence turning and begin to go right down. They drilled sixty-five feet in the rock and the drill got kinda dragging to what it had been doing, not running smooth. So they pulled out and examined it and they found that one of the cones had chipped and locked. So he carried it to the shop at Batson and I cleaned everything away. He taken it back and finished drilling through the rock which was one hundred and thirty-four feet deep. That was the first use.

[J. Edgar] Pew, the Sun Company man here, was telling [Walter] Sharp about my having this drill that he'd used in drilling this well. So Sharp had Pew delayed there. He called Hughes and told Hughes, says, "Wynn's got a rock drill at Batson. I want you to go get it and not come back without it."

So Hughes went to Batson to the shop and told this foreman that he had a hard rock up at Shreveport and that he couldn't drill it with a rotary, and he wanted to borrow it to take it up there. My foreman let him have it and instead of Hughes taking it to Shreveport, he taken it to Houston. Well, when he got it to Houston the engineers and the mechanics in the laboratories soon saw the working of the drill and what the result would be in it and they remodeled and made the Sharp-Hughes roller bit. So then Sharp had Hughes to come to Beaumont here, make a deal, bought the patent from me. He paid me six thousand dollars.

Not being in the invention business and everything and all, and knowing the fault of my idea, that I could see that didn't operate right, and wasn't in a position to explore and make a success out of it, I thought to help development and conditions, that six thousand dollars was that much and would cause some other source to carry on the patent.

And I sold the patent in 1909.

—*John S. Wynn*

SHARP: Speaking of Mr. Hughes, I've always heard so many different kind of stories about that rock bit, and when it started, and who started it, and who really invented it, and how it came into existence, I wonder if you can remember anything about that, either one of you?

CULLINAN: I think I can tell you exactly.

SHARP: I certainly would like to hear it because I never—

PRATHER: I know I can.

CULLINAN: Huh?

PRATHER: Go ahead.

CULLINAN: It was your father's idea, his alone.

PRATHER: No.

CULLINAN: All right. [Laughter] I know we disagree.

PRATHER: No, not—it was his [Walter B. Sharp's] idea about the rock bit. But the rock bit, somebody over in Louisiana had made this bit and he'd seen one of them and looked at it, and he thought —when he got to running into this rock—he thought it'd do pretty good. But it was just a sort of a fishtail rock bit, you know.

CULLINAN: Wasn't nothing like the bit that was developed.

PRATHER: No, and when he organized the—what was that company?

SHARP: Moonshine?

PRATHER: No, it wasn't the Moonshine then.

SHARP: Producers?

CULLINAN: No, it was something else.

PRATHER: Anyway, Howard Hughes got interested in the bit and Walter just called it the Sharp-Hughes Tool Company and turned it over to Howard, and he worked it out and made it what it was.

CULLINAN: That's exactly what I was going to say.

PRATHER: Yes, yes.

CULLINAN: It was his idea strictly, now, disregarding this Louisiana man. He wasn't in it at all. It came right out of Walter Sharp's brain, the idea. But he was not an engineer, and he couldn't develop it. He couldn't make it cut the full size or anything like that.

So he got Howard Hughes, who was an excellent engineer, to develop the bit, and Sharp and J. S. Cullinan had the financial end of the bit. Of course, it's nothing like the bit today.

SHARP: Well, it's a funny thing about that, Mr. Cullinan. I remember we used to have a little sample of one of the early bits at home, and it was a little sharp bit with two cones on it like they have.

CULLINAN: Little two cones—

SHARP: And then they developed later on into this great enormous bit with the Acme lubricator, the Acme bit, big tremendous things, I remember.

CULLINAN: Yes.

SHARP: Stand about six feet high sometimes, a long lubricator. And now they've gone back to a bit which, as I remember it, was little—

CULLINAN: Yes.

SHARP: It's a little sharp bit again—

CULLINAN: Yes.

SHARP: Like the original bit was.

CULLINAN: Yes.

SHARP: Isn't that true?

CULLINAN: That's true.

SHARP: So—

CULLINAN: This—this had a lubricator in. The Texas Company developed a special grease in their refineries to lubricate this bit. It had a lubricator—a small pipe was all it was, with a plunger on the end of it. It was fifteen or twenty feet long, the original. And when they brought it out and tried it out on Producers Oil Company's wells, they took them to north Texas where we had more heavy rock. And Howard Hughes would bring the bit out, and he'd put it in, and even the crew didn't know what it was.

SHARP: I understand there was a lot of secrecy about it.

CULLINAN: Oh, yes, indeed.

SHARP: They'd wrap it up in a gunny sack or something, and then bring it out, and then they'd lower it down.

CULLINAN: Old people would put it in. After it got in the hole—

SHARP: Lower it in the hole then—

CULLINAN: Then they'd go ahead and turn it back to the drillers. [Laughter]

PRATHER: I never heard of that.

CULLINAN: Well, I worked under those. I know.

SHARP: Well, that's very interesting. I've always wanted to hear just exactly how that happened.

CULLINAN: It was just one of those things that took an engineer to develop.

—Dudley C. Sharp, Frank Cullinan, and Ed Prather

Yes, I used the roller bit at Ged, Louisiana, out of Vinton there, in 1908. Old man Howard Hughes and our superintendent, who was Mr. H. A. Millett, they brought a bit down in a sack. Well, then they pulled out, they run all the crew off. They didn't want anybody to see it. The two and myself put the bit on, stuck it back in the hole, and they come in, we went on down and dulled that one and come out and changed the cones on it and went back with another one. Well, in about seven hours we'd worn out two sets of cones and a whole bit.

It was awful hard formation. We went ahead and took a core of that later, and there's about, oh I guess, about twenty-five per cent of it was pyrites, pyrites of iron.

He probably didn't have it perfected at that time, because they didn't let everybody see one of them. And at that time, of course, they dressed those bits, they call them. They carried the cones along, took them to pieces and put new cones on them. Now those cones are welded on there and whenever you dull one of them, why they pick it up. You just pay for the cones and dull them and then they pick them up and take them back and if they're in good shape they redress them themselves; take them to pieces and put them back and will give you a new one.

We used to buy the bits then and they were a good bit on the same shape they are now. They were short and had three cones on them, and later on they made a taller bit with reamers on them and then finally got up to where they was something like three foot long. Had side reamers on it to keep your hole in good shape as you went. And when they come back about every twenty years they change it a little. I guess that's to keep their patent going. They've improved it quite a lot, because those teeth on them now are as much as a inch long and they interlock that way and keep the formation cleaned out of them.

The cones rotate. They are put on a perfect circle and when they set down, why they just roll on the formation and chip it. Been a big improvement in that in recent years.

When Howard Hughes got hold of that patent, Walter Sharp really put up the money and it was called Sharp and Hughes and they were out here on the north side, and then after Sharp died, Hughes bought his interest out. It was the Hughes Tool Company from then on. Then they got into all other kinds of manufacturing, valves, tool joints, and general oil-field equipment. First it was just a roller-bit outfit, just made roller bits, what we call roller bits or rock bits.

—*J. A. Rush*

I guess I know about as much about the invention of the rock bit as anybody outside of Howard Hughes, Ed Prather, or somebody like that, some of them fellows.

We had a terrible time, you know. Our bits wasn't any good, to speak of, you know. Just ordinary steel tempered, and water and oil, and they'd wear out quick. And it was a big trouble to change them. And some fellows at Sour Lake, Johnny Wynn and some fellows— Johnny claims it, but Johnny didn't do nothing but put up the men. Old McLaughlin, him and another fellow—I forget that other fellow's name now—was really the fellows that made the bit. And the Union Sulphur Company had a crude affair of a bit. And old Newmanson had a crude affair at Shreveport then, which would develop the Reed Roller Bit out of the patent.

Howard Hughes hadn't made a success in the oil business, that was a cinch. But he was a pretty good engineer. Pretty good dreamer, you know. And Walter [Sharp] knew it and he bought all these patents up and turned Howard loose to make a rock bit. Turned Hughes loose for a half interest, you know. Mrs. Sharp sold her half interest to Ed Prather. And then Ed finally sold out to Howard because—said Howard run him crazy, the way he'd do business, you know. Nobody but old Howard made a lot of money out of it. And that was one of the first of this rock-bit business, you know.

—*Benjamin Coyle*

Poor Man's Packer

Well, them days they didn't know much about cementin' and they didn't ever cement, and it's different from these days. These days lots of times they drill right on through the sand with a big bit and set the pipes on the bottom of the hole and cement it and then perforate the pipe. But them days they didn't know enough to do that, you know. They thought they had to have a shoulder to set that pipe on, on top of the pay formation. In case they couldn't have a shoulder, we'd set a packer in the hole.

I've made a many a packer myself—what they call a poor man's packer. I believe I can set a string of pipe in any hole I've ever seen and make it hold without cementing it. The poor man's packer—the way I make them, I put them right on the pipe just above the shoe. I take about three or four yards of canvas. I wrap it real tight right around that pipe, and then I take about a hundred, hundred twenty-five feet of quarter-inch rope and wrap it real tight. And you wrap it real tight around the bottom part of that canvas. Then when you get it on, you go around and about every three rounds, you nail it, with little shingle nails, through one coil and into another, and so on that way till you get to the top. When you get it on there, it's on to stay; it won't come off.

When I get it all fixed, then I take a knife and split this canvas at the top into strips, just strip it down to the top of that rope. Strips anywhere from six inches to a foot's all right. Then I take it and put it back up around the pipe, smooth as I can, and tie it with a couple of strands of salt line up at the top, to hold it up till it gets in the hole. I always made a seven-inch o.d. casing when I'd make a packer. When I'd offset the hole to look for the [oil-bearing] sand, I'd find the sand and I'd ram the hole down within three feet of the top of the sand. Then I'd pull out and put on a seven-and-seven-eighths bit, just a little bit bigger than the shoe on this casing. That packer and shoe sets down in that three feet of seven-and-seven-eighths hole, it's in there tight; then the loose part at the top, it'll bag down all around that pipe, little stuff settle around it. I can make pipe hold in darn near any hole I ever saw that way. The mud and cavings will come in on it. In fact, I've set a many of them that way. I've set hundreds that way. I don't think I ever did have one fail to hold.

—J. T. (Cotton) Young

Early Method of Cementing

I did some of the first cementing jobs that I ever heard of being done down in Louisiana. We'd do the cementing ourselves. You know Halliburton'd been cementing wells in this country a long

time, and all over the country. But this was before his time. We
cemented ourselves down in Louisiana once in a while. We'd put the
cement in and pump it down. Now they use a little plug—Halliburton
does—about eight inches long, to put in behind the cement. When
he gets the cement pumped in, well, he puts this plug in behind it,
you see, to pump the cement down with.

Them days we'd go out there and cut a pine sapling, right
straight slim pine sapling, just about the size of the casing, and peel
the bark all off of it. We'd make them fifteen feet long, and boy,
was they a bearcat to drill up! They was something to drill up—those
little old green pine saplings, you couldn't hardly drill them up. But
that's the way they done; that's all they knew. They thought there
had to be a big long plug. Put it in behind the cement and put the
pump on and pumped it down.

I cemented lots of wells for McMan Oil Company. And I cemented them with just twenty sacks of cement. I'd have my shoe
fixed before I put it on the pipe to run it. I'd have three little quarter-
inch pins. I'd have holes drilled in that shoe and let them little
quarter-inch pins stick out inside the shoe about an inch. And I
wouldn't run a very long plug, run about a two-foot plug. The reason
I did that, when I went to pump the cement down, I didn't have
no way to run steel line behind it like Halliburton does, you know.
But I never failed to know when the plug was down, and I don't
think I ever failed to get a cement job.

When you pump the cement in, run it in, and put this plug in
behind it, I always cut a couple of pieces of belting just the size of
the pipe and nailed it on the top of that plug. I'd put in and put
about a third of the sack of sand on top of it, and put the pump on
and start pumping. I'd just let the old pump go wide open till she
hit bottom. When she hit bottom, when that plug hit them pins in
that shoe, it'd just stop it like that and I'd shut the pump off.

Well, you knew then that the cement was all behind the pipe
and the plug was on bottom and everything was fine. Then you just
set the pipe down and went off and left it. You had to suspend the
pipe, usually about a foot off the bottom, till you finished pumping
the cement out of it. And most of the time you had to keep the pipe
moving a little bit all the time, up and down or something, to keep
it from sticking. You had to keep moving a little bit all the time to
keep it from sticking. But I've made lots of cement jobs like that.

—*J. T. (Cotton) Young*

Invention of the Cable Core Barrel

Mr. Robichaux was a farmer around here [in Beaumont], rice farmer, and a good mechanic. He was always trying to invent something, especially in the oil-drilling-equipment way. He had an old tractor the last time I saw him in the field, and he had it rigged up with a small rotary, and he was drilling a well a thousand or twelve hundred feet deep with this little contraption.

One day he came up to my office, and says, "Well, I've made a wonderful thing for the oil business. Instead of pulling out all the drill pipe, change your bits—why I've rigged up a cable and a core barrel; it'll work with a steam engine on the drilling-rig floor with a big drum. If you've got a well ten thousand feet deep and you want to core it, all you have to do is put your core barrel on and drop it down in your drill stem, and have a hole in your bit. This will go through the bit and then self-lock. Then you go ahead and drill if you've taken an eight- or ten- or twelve-foot core, or any length that you desire. And when you drill to that depth—why, then you'd give this wire line a sudden jerk from the derrick floor, and that would release the pin that was holding it down in the bit. In about five minutes you'd have it up on the derrick floor, open it up, take a look at the sands, or whatever you wanted to look at what's in the core barrel."

I saw the first one that he constructed and had operating. It was on the Shell Oil Company's well north of Hampshire, right south of Gilbert Ranch here. I went down there one afternoon to take a look at it, as he'd offered me a half interest in the core barrel for seventy-five hundred dollars. I stood around there quite a while, talked to the driller and the gang pusher on the rig, asking them about this core barrel and how the recovery was on it and how it worked. They went on to explain at times you'd get a small piece of core and lots of times you'd get nothing. They rather discouraged me, so I came on back and the next day Mr. Robichaux came in and asked me what I thought about it, and I told him what they said out there. And then I told him I wouldn't be interested in it.

He then went over and got the Reed Roller Bit Company interested in this core barrel. They bought the core barrel and let him retain a royalty. This core barrel is used extensively yet. Practically any drilling rig that you go on in this part of the country—why, you'll see the old Robichaux barrel there and it's working. It made the Reed Company quite a fortune, and also Mr. Robichaux, who is now dead.

—W. C. *Gilbert*

Coring a Salt Dome

The bosses, in the meantime, had provided us with heavy oak wooden boxes made out of two-inch oak and about eight or ten feet long, and, as I recall it, they had two hasps and two padlocks on each one. And we'd go down and take a core.

In order to get this core we had a drill head on the bottom of this hydraulic pipe and the cutting was made possible by the offset setting into this corehead of black diamonds. They set one to cut outside and then one to catch the inside just a little bit. I understood the value of them was twenty-eight hundred dollars. I know we lost one of them and never did recover it, and that's the reason I happen to know what they estimated the cost. We finally decided that we could—by changing them more frequently—get the job done with parts of a file, so we'd get a new file, a flat file, and break it up and drill a little place in these core shoes, and then set these pieces of file in there and then fastened them in and did very good with it. We cored this sulphur and got sulphur in each of the wells and put it in these boxes.

In the third well, we had been ordered to drill deeper, drill through the sulphur, see what there was below it. So we cored the sulphur and ran the core and didn't get anything. And he said, "Now, Walter, that's the salt dome they've been looking for." And I said, "Well, I don't see how you could tell. All we got is just a slick bunch of pipe. Ain't a thing in the world in it, not a thing." And he said, "Well, I'll prove it to you because I'll have to demonstrate it to our employers." Said, "You go down to Mr. Bryan's and get his wagon and team and go over to Velasco and buy all the salt you can find. Buy all the blocks of salt, lick salt for cattle. Buy all the rock salt. And when you get through with that, why, just commence buying table salt in sacks, nickel sacks or four-bit sacks or fifty-pound sacks. Just buy a wagonload of salt."

Well, while I was gone, the old gentleman had made a little box on the derrick floor, watertight; had calked the cracks and fixed the circulation and we backed this wagonload of salt up and unloaded it on the derrick floor and started a slow trickle of water in this box. We'd stir with a couple of hoes that box full of water and salt until the water wouldn't absorb any more salt. It was just as salty as the salt was, in other words. Then we'd pump that in. Then we'd make up another batch and pump that in. Well, we finally got enough salt water to get a return. The water that came out was salty so we knew we had a hole full and the pipe full of salt. Then he took a core and he pulled out the prettiest, smoothest core of crystal salt you ever saw. The water before had melted the salt as fast as we cut it and when he got the brine in there, with just as much salt in it as there was salt, then he could take a core, and he took a core.

—*Walter Cline*

A Fishing Job

I've sat nights and figured on these old fishing jobs and draw pictures of just the shape I'd think the fishing job would be in the hole, you know. I'd draw pictures of the tools I was going to run and everything and try to figure out what to do. I did some good fishing jobs, if I do say it myself. I cleaned out lots of old holes that ordinarily they might've lost, if somebody hadn't cleaned them out.

I was called down there to Moran to fish out a string of three-inch tubing that they had pulled in two on this old gas well. I had used everything that I had that I could think of to try to get the old tubing out. All I could think of was a string of left-handed pipe. I knew the tubing was split open at the top; it didn't have any collar on the top of it. Couldn't get nothing in it to hold it and you couldn't get nothing over it.

A bunch of the Texas Company officials come there. I didn't know they was in town, but I had just got to my row's end at the rig and I'd walked into town to talk things over with somebody. Fellow by the name of Morter was the bookkeeper, and I walked in the office and he told me, said, "Mr. Cullinan and Mr. Sharp and a whole bunch of them are in the other office there."

And I said, "They are?"

He said, "yeah." Well, I wasn't there long till Frank Cullinan come out in the office for something and of course he talked to me, asked me how I's getting along. I said, "I'm not doing no good. I think I'm going to have to have a string of left-handed pipe out there before I'll ever get that old tubing out. It's busted open on the top.

I can't get nothing to hold in it and I can't get nothing over it, and the only thing I know is to get a string of left-handed pipe and screw that bad joint off the top and get it out of there. Then maybe I can get ahold of it with something and pull it out."

And he says, "Well, Cotton, we just got one string of left-handed pipe in the whole country, and that's that string there at Electra."

I said, "Well, I got one more thing I'd like to try before you send it down here." And he wanted to know what it was and I told him.

He'd [Mr. Sharp] get you anything you wanted that he thought you needed. He'd always do that. And so Frank told me, Mr. Cullinan told me, said, "Well, you get on the train and go to Electra and have Denny"—that was Denny Hill, the shop foreman at Electra—"have Denny to make that thing like you want it and stay there till they get it made and then get on the train with it and come right along with it on the way down here, to see that it don't get dumped off somewhere and laid over."

I stayed around two or three days—watching, keeping in touch with Denny—before they ever got that spear ready to send out and when it come through, I was at the depot to see that it got on the right train going to Moran, you know, and see that they didn't lay it over. They put it on the train all right, so I got on the train and we went to Stamford, and there was a chance of getting laid over there. But I watched it through there and it didn't get laid over there. So I went right on to Moran then.

I took it out there and run it. It was a spear—I'd never seen a longer one or heard of one like that before in my life. It was twenty-three feet long, and it was a three-inch bulldog spear, made out of a just a solid bar of iron, about two-inch iron, you know. There was a connection on top of it to screw the drill pipe to, and then a mandrel and slip on the bottom end of it to get ahold in a three-inch width.

The slip has teeth in it and it fits on a mandrel; this mandrel's tapering, you know, and you get ahold on the pipe, of course, when you run it in there and this slips free, it'll run up and down on the mandrel, but when you run it in there and get ahold on the pipe, why the harder you pull, why the more that slip pulls down on the taper of the mandrel, the bigger it gets, you know, the harder hold it gets. They call that bulldog spear. So I made that thing and took it out there and got ahold.

Next morning there's plenty of pressure all right. I was standing outside pulling, out by the side of the engine, and I run up against it pretty stiff, and it wouldn't move a inch. When I reversed it to slack off, it run backwards and I couldn't get the old reverse lever back down. It run off about six feet of slack, and I finally yanked her back down. When I did and it started the other way, I didn't shut nothing off. I just let her go. It run up against it that time. The thing just come like that, you know, up three or four inches at a jump. I knew I had her whipped then, and it just kept coming that way all the way out of the hole.

The top of that three-inch didn't have any collar on the top of it, that made the top of it weak. I'd been in the top of it with a spear of the same kind only shorter, and every time I'd go in there —well, I'd get ahold—but when I'd pull on it, it'd just rip its way out, just split the pipe and go right on. With this twenty-three-foot spear I could run clean down through the top joint and get ahold right under the collar of the second joint, you see. That made it a whole lot stronger, and it was strong enough so that it stood the gaff all right till I got it out of the hole.

—J. T. (Cotton) Young

Acidization

Nitroglycerin was the only way to loosen up pay strata, and get oil out of it. You know, a lot of times you'll see something that's so darn easy and so simple that you wonder why you hadn't—or a million people hadn't—thought of it a hundred years before. Well, we had used acid; I had done it myself, and have seen geologists do it around where we were drilling a well.

You reclaimed some sand, and they want to know how much sand it contained and how much lime. Take hydrochloric acid and burn the lime out to see how much of the sand was left. Why some knucklehead hadn't thought of the idea of putting some of that down in that hole to do the work of the nitroglycerin where lime was present! Why didn't somebody think of that? Why didn't some guy know enough of chemistry, by golly, to have tried that a hundred years ago?

—E. P. Matteson

Underwater Drilling

I went to South Louisiana and took headquarters at Lake Charles. At that time the only so-called water operations in South

Texas or South Louisiana was at Hackberry, near Lake Charles, south of Sulphur, Louisiana. Some of these wells were on mats in the marshy ground and the Louisiana Land Exploration Company had one well out in about four or five feet of water. And that was built with a board mat in the bottom of the bay mud and then cribbing of timbers to get the height for the rig. That's about all there was in water development that I knew of.

Some of the waters were twelve and fourteen feet deep. I didn't know anything about it. We didn't have any engineers that knew anything about it. I conferred with different people, construction engineers in New Orleans that were building those big buildings there. The chief engineer of the L & N Railroad, Mr. Corbett, was very helpful to me and he advised piling in every instance. We drew our own plans and details for piling operations for steam rigs or, in some of the waters that were seven feet deep, we still used mats.

We found after the first mats—by putting those mats board to board—sometimes the vibration of those rigs made them slip, even without any equipment on them. I got the idea that I used snowshoes in Canada and I didn't slip with snowshoes. I did slip with skis. So the mats were laid with a break of four inches between each board and when that would settle through the silt and muck of the bottom, the mat never would slip after that. And to make the derricks level, we put steel plates, three or four of them, under each corner of the derrick legs with a slot, like a U-bolt, so that if one side of the derrick went down, you wouldn't build up on that leg. You'd go pull out [plates] on the opposite leg.

We found that line derricks wasn't very successful. For the piling operations we drove group pilings and laced them and put three guy lines from each corner of the derrick. But someway, waves or vibration, you could not keep those guy lines at all. Same thing with the mat. And so then we would tie the derricks, each leg to the foundations. With the piling, we belted the post group under each corner with a bar under that belt and a big rod up into a plate at the base of the derrick leg. That meant if a derrick went to go over, the whole thing would have to pull fifty-two piling maybe, which is not very easy to do.

We would lay four- or six-inch old pipe, eight or nine feet long, under before we put the mat down with a big rod up through that laying horizontal with the ground and that would fasten the derrick down to that mat. There's an awful lot of suction hold to anything laying in mud unless air can get into it. So we did away with the guying entirely and that was one of our problems, trying to keep the derricks from blowing over. There was semiequinox storms that we used to have.

Those things we worked out and, finally, before I was through with the whole operation and came back to Houston, we had nine producing fields and we had built our first two drilling barges and some of us thought we originated the idea of a submerged barge.

Now, floating drilling barges was something that had been in existence for a long time. They used them in the Hudson for the sounding for the tunnels. And a young Frenchman named Leguerre drilled wells for sulphur at Jefferson Lake out of New Iberia in nontideland water where the barges floated. They were stationary with big posts that go down into the water from the barge. And when we started our first barge, we built one similar. And we took it down to the mouth of the Mississippi River and the problem there was tides two or three feet a day. When the tide would run out, it would bend our tie-downs on the barge and we'd be out of the center of the hole. We took a barge and put some boilers on it with the idea of submerging it. And some of our associates weren't very keen for that test but we did it and we drilled several wells by sinking the barge on the bottom of seven, eight, or nine feet of water. When we'd want to move, we just pumped water out of the different bulkheads and the barge floated and we'd tow it away and sink it again.

Then the idea came, the drilling rig on a barge that would submerge and be floated. And we found that the idea was patented by an Italian Merchant Marine captain. At the end of eighteen months or so, they located him, and the Texas Company bought the patents. And they can let anybody build them. They pay the Texas Company so much for the permission to build the barges.

That was the beginning and I stayed until we had first of the bigger drilling barges into operation. I never drilled out in the Gulf of Mexico as they're doing today. It was really kindergarten work compared to the present-day operations.

—*Alexander Balfour Patterson*

Drilling on Submerged Land

At that time they were drilling all along the banks of the Caddo Lake in Louisiana and Texas. Then Gulf I believe was the first I ever heard of that drilled out in water. They drilled a well in twenty-five to forty foot of water. They did that by building pile drivers and they drove piling for all these rigs—for the rotary rig and the boilers and all foundation for the pump station, and for the tanks and for the mud pit, because the Levee Board of Texas or Louisiana wouldn't allow any oil or mud or anything to go into the water to where it would interfere with fish.

It cost lots of money because they had to have barges to haul this stuff and they went up about eighteen miles to some land they bought in Texas, called Potter Land, and they cut this piling up there, their cyprus piling. When I left there to come out to the West here, why they had two hundred and forty-five wells out in that lake, all of them on piling.

—Frank Hamilton

The First Whipstock

The first whipstock was ever made, I had it made at Orange. We had a blowout and pipe dropped back and mashed, and we couldn't sidetrack it, couldn't fish it out, so we worked there for a long time and then I designed the first whipstock. I didn't patent it and there's no patent on the whipstock today except Kinchback here in Houston, he come out and made one with a loose joint in it and some dogs on it where you could set it anywhere you wanted it, see.

Well, now, he got a patent on that one but it's on the kind of whipstock. Mine was just regular old cast-iron whipstock that makes you go outside your pipe, change your direction; and when I come to Goose Creek for the company, they had a lot of wells that had gone on down and hit water and everything, and [that was] my job when I come there was to take over so many rigs, so many men, to mill out those so they could go on down and look for deeper stuff. That was what I first done before I took charge of the drilling there. That was the only thing I had. We didn't have all the fancy fishing tools and the milling equipment them days we have now.

But it was in what's known as the Ged field in Louisiana in 1911 that I first used a whipstock. It didn't take very long to make it. The superintendent didn't think it was going to be worth anything. I told him I thought he could mill it out in a week. But we milled it out and were making our hole in twenty-four hours.

—J. A. Rush

Air Lifting

They started as soon as the gushers [at Spindletop] began to fail. Everybody was putting in that air. We installed them in this station of ours—two large air compressors, and of course they didn't last long. It did very well as long as it had fluid, but as soon as the oil was out it was no good and they started moving to Sour Lake. They thought it [Spindletop] was gone, and it produced more oil afterward than it did before.

—R. R. *Hobson*

Later, Frank C. Henderson put in an air-compressor plant, the first one that I know of in the field [Spindletop]. And he would get well owners to let him try blowing them with air, for a per cent of the increase. One particular well that I was operating was pumping eight hundred and eighty barrels a day, of eighty-cent oil. And I objected to shutting it down to let Henderson's outfit experiment with it, but he agreed to pay all the costs of pulling out, pulling the well, and installing his equipment, a trial to see if he'd better the production any, for which he was to get twenty-five per cent, I think, of the increase.

And it was not a success. It didn't increase us any, and we put her back to pumping. Henderson paid the expense. I don't think we were losing anything, because we made about as much oil as we had been making during the period that he tried it.

The air-compressor system did become a success later. Very much so. In a Humble field years afterward, in 1915 or '16, I think, they had big flowing wells brought in around three thousand feet, make fourteen thousand or fifteen thousand barrels. And when the pressure got off, and those wells quit flowing, the companies and independents who had wells scouted the country and bought up old air compressors that hadn't been in use in the oil fields for years. But there were some few of them in the rice country, Louisiana and Texas, where they'd been blowing wells. And they brought them to Humble and installed them and blew the wells and brought them back to big production.

Yes, that was what we called the deep stuff at Humble at that time. They produced fine, those air compressors. With all the expense of hauling them and setting them up, they'd pay for themselves in twenty-four hours in the production.

—*Early C. Deane*

Recycling

In the wells drilled in Seminole field [in 1924], mostly there were not enough reservoir pressures to make the wells flow, so they floated them with what they called at first the air lifter. That's what they used at first. They'd compress air and put it down in the hole and through the casing and blow oil out through the tubing, or vice versa. Then they found pretty soon that that was kind of dangerous so they changed to gas, and they recycled the gas then, and we produced some natural gasoline that way with the compression and pooling of the gas as we recycled it. That was quite a bit of our connection with the production of oil. We worked a little while on a lift station. That's what they called the stations that done the pressuring to lift the oil, where we also done the switching of the oil, or, in other words, took the place of the pumper.

—*James L. Delaplain*

FROM

GAME

TO

BUSINESS

11

Within the last thirty years the oil industry has attained relative stability. An orderly development has replaced the periodic chaos that formerly occurred when the discovery of a new field created boom towns and often flooded the market with oil that sold for less than water, and wasteful methods left more oil in the ground than was recovered. The industry, however, is not static. Expansion continues at a rate sufficient to meet the demand for energy to heat our houses, propel our cars, trucks, airplanes, ships, and locomotives, and to supply basic substances for an expanding petrochemical industry. Of the more than twelve million barrels of crude that reach our refineries daily, about thirty per cent is imported. In order to prevent physical and economic waste, the domestic wells are allowed to produce at about thirty per cent potential.

This orderly production has been made possible by the development of instruments for securing the data necessary to determine the best procedures for obtaining the maximum recovery in any field and by the revision of state and federal laws to make enforcement of these procedures possible. The geological formation, the reservoir fluid, the oil-gas ratio, and the bottom-hole pressure are some of the factors taken into account in determining well spacing and allowable production and in estimating the total recovery, upon which financial credit is based.

The cost of drilling has steadily increased, not only because of the increased cost of equipment, but also because as the shallow pools are exhausted, oil is being sought in deep formations revealed by geophysics and subsurface geology. A 13,000-foot well drilled on land costs as much as six 5000-foot wells. Off-shore drilling is even more expensive. One hole drilled 13,386 feet in the Gulf of Mexico near Galveston cost approximately a million dollars. It was dry.

The cost of drilling exploratory wells has restricted the operations of the independent wildcatter of modest means. He survives, however, partly through a cooperative arrangement called bottom-hole pay, by which other operators, often major companies, who have leases nearby agree to pay part of the cost of drilling provided the well is dry. In that case, they have in effect paid a specified sum for the geological information the well yields.

Improvements in drilling equipment have been spectacular. At the beginning of the century the driller was directly dependent upon his senses. He surmised what was going on under the ground largely by the feel of the cable, or by the sound and speed of the rotary. His hole was seldom truly vertical—indeed, instances are on record of bits from rigs hundreds of yards apart meeting hundreds of feet under the ground. Now a gyroscopic device keeps the drill pipe in a vertical position, and unintentional deviation is no defense in court. Directional drilling, however, permitted under certain circumstances, can be done with great accuracy. Instruments show at all times the weight of the drill pipe resting on the bottom, the speed of the rotary, the weight suspended on the derrick, and the pressure on the mud pumps. Mud is tested for filtration loss, viscosity, and gel strength, and corrections are made when needed. Off-shore drilling rigs of several types, all expensive, are in use.

This complex equipment has changed the nature of oil-field work and thus the character of the workman. The old jokes about strong backs and weak minds have lost whatever applicability they may once have had. No longer is it necessary for the oil-field worker to live on location. He may drive fifty or sixty miles each way to work. Rest breaks may be spent on the derrick floor. More likely they are spent in air-conditioned trailers with television and indoor toilets.

Strictly a Gamble

The difference between oil operations in those days of Batson and Humble and Sour Lake and Spindletop and as of the present day is that in those days it was a game, strictly a gamble. Nobody had any scientific data or information nor wanted any. They wouldn't have believed a fellow if he'd a told them. They just used the hunt and peck and look system and let the best man win. And today it's a highly technical business, down to a point where it's far too complicated and too much involved with experts and advisers for me to ever make a success of trying to operate it. I could play it when it was a game. I know how to play games, but I'm not very good at a technical business, and a game was what we had in the early days in the oil field.

Then the technicians and the fellows—the Phi Beta Kappas—began to make themselves felt. And to the benefit of the oil industry. I have no objection or criticism of it. I do sometimes have just a little twinge of regret that we've lost the romance and heroism and the flavor of the good old days. There were enough stories in one boom oil field to write a hundred books about. We have now the satisfaction of knowing that we're producing more oil from deeper horizons at less expense and less waste and everything else, which is all to the good from the standpoint of the nation and the individual citizen. But for us old-timers, it's just a different way of getting the job done.

—*Walter Cline*

Worker to Manager

Some of them, you know, developed into very good machinists and very competent men. And you take the average man that works in the oil field, that tries to do something, he proves to be competent, and he is the man that is now the head of these oil companies.

At that time, the oil business was new, so to speak; and, it was a remark I've heard it said, it took a weak mind and a strong back to do the work. But the people in the oil business at that time, they didn't have to have the education that they do today. In other words, the operation then wasn't scientific like it is now. We done things then in the oil fields and in drilling wells and everything of that sort that people would laugh at us now if you'd want to do that kind of work in that way.

Very, very primitive. The men of that time was very limited in education, they realized that they had to apply themselves to get anywhere, and long and faithful service went a long ways with these companies.

And, in other words, what they knew about the oil business and what they later had to come in contact with, their knowledge was the experience in the school of hard knocks. They learned by actual experience, and I have noted at that time that I knew men was drillers that could not keep a log of their drilling well, and they would hire their roustabouts or their roughnecks that had an education to keep the log book for him and his makings. But for him to do it, he couldn't have done it. And them men proved to be very good men in the work. And when it come to drilling a well or pumping a well or anything, they knew thoroughly, and I would say that whenever anything taken place in the experience of a well, it was something that they remembered.

—*James Donohoe*

Father and Son

My son was down here the other day. He was born in 1909, and I'm very proud of the boy. But something unusual—he's a lot more conservative than his daddy is. Now he don't get out on a limb on any of these things around here. He wants to be on the safe side of everything, and I was always on the other side. I drilled many a well by myself just because I thought I was going to get an oil well.

But he wouldn't no more do that than nothing. But he was down here the other day and I said, "Son, I see oil went up thirty-five cents a barrel." He says, "Yes, and you know why?" And I said, "No." He says, "They're shipping so much oil from Venezuela over here, nine million three hundred thousand barrels a day, and these producers in this country were making so much complaint about it, they decided they better give us thirty-five cents a barrel and shut our mouths."

—*Claude Witherspoon*

Geology and Geophysics

John Lovejoy was the general manager of Amerada [Oil Company] at that time and now is the president of Seaboard Oil. He was an engineer by training; of course, would say that he was not a geologist, but as a matter of fact, there is very little oil geology that he doesn't know a great deal about.

[Everette Lee] DeGolyer, he was the president of Amerada at that time, and of course is one of the outstanding oil geologists of this country, definitely. I think [he] brought over the first gravity balance, and I think he was very influential in using seismic shooting also. Yes, I would say that he is one of the pioneers in employing geophysical methods in finding oil, if not perhaps *the* pioneer in some phase of it. Of course, a vast amount of that has been done in subsequent years. And a good many refinements, but, of course, today the engineering involved in producing oil requires the use of almost all of the scientists—chemists, physicists, paleontologists, mathematicians. It's now carried on very scientifically, and they don't miss many bets. I would say that they are far ahead of the mining industry in their use of science in discovering resources.

They drill dry holes because there is no way of predicting whether you have oil or whether you do not have oil. You may predict whether you have a favorable trap for oil, but no geophysical method has yet been discovered to tell you whether oil is beneath you or not. Oil traps, measured against the vast expanse of the area over which you work, are so small that there's plenty of chance to miss it.

Today I think you'll drill ten or eleven oil wells before you strike one. I forget exactly what the percentage is today, but it's a matter of record. It's recorded every year, the number of dry holes against the ones that are successful.

—Sidney Paige

Financing

Now I may say that at the present time about eighty per cent of our work consists of evaluation work in estimating underground oil and gas reserves. These estimates are used primarily by buyers and sellers of oil properties and banks for loan purposes. The operator submits the reports to the banks and borrows money based on the amount of reserves that we estimate that he can recover from his leases. And that eighty per cent of the business that is transacted on oil loans is based upon engineering reports at the present times. There has been quite a change in that in the twenty-five or thirty years that I have been in this profession. In the early days the geologist was not looked upon as being much more than a doodle-bug. His guess was just a little better than the operator's, but the operator usually would not admit it. Now it is recognized as a means for actually transacting business. And no bank would consider making a substantial loan on an oil property now without an engineering report on the reserves.

When I came to East Texas, the banks in Tyler were not at all familiar with the oil business. And they would not make oil loans to any extent at all. And in 1935, '34 I believe, I was made a director of the Tyler State Bank and Trust Company, primarily due to the fact that I had information on the value of oil properties and the bank wanted to extend its services to the oil industry. And that has been a means of me aiding the bank considerably and the bank aiding me considerably. It was a mutual and profitable operation for both of us. And our bank, the Tyler State Bank and Trust Company, as well as the other two banks in Tyler, carry large oil-banking business now, much larger than the average banks of their size throughout Texas. It's now recognized throughout the whole nation.

Many loans are made in New York and Chicago and very distant points on nothing but the engineer's reports on the property. And even banks that have not set up an oil department will frequently refer from one bank to another as to who to get to make engineering reports. And for that reason it is pretty important that anyone in the consulting business get well acquainted with the bankers in his area.

—*James S. Hudnall*

Dry-hole Pay

This is by way of illustration, that even with the deep drilling and so forth, it's possible for the little fellow to still get along. Shell was drawing their acreage and there we were left with two hundred acres with a three-sixteenths royalty. Joe Zeffler was going to drill on half of it, one hundred acres, but with the additional acreage and forty thousand dollars from the Shell and some other money we'd raised—but to make a long story short, we pressed the issue and didn't want to give it up entirely, and the Shell raised their dry-hole contribution to a hundred thousand dollars, which, plus what we had already had from the other companies, Joe Zeffler took and drilled a ten-thousand-foot hole on the hundred-acre tract, a wildcat well. It was a dry hole, but nevertheless we didn't have the money to drill it and yet we got a ten-thousand-foot hole drilled in the toughest part of East Texas. And on the other hand, while it was only a two-hundred-acre tract, they had a hundred acres, and we had a hundred; they came out about even with the dry-hole contributions they had and a hundred acres of oil land that was worth a lot of money, if it happened to hit.

—*E. I. Thompson*

Proration in East Texas

HAYES: When the great East Texas oil field was discovered in 1930, one of the first serious economic problems was the unrestricted production of oil, which at one time brought the price down to as low as ten cents a barrel. The East Texas Chamber of Commerce, under the leadership of Hubert M. Harrison as general manager, realized the necessity of finding a solution to this problem, and realized that overproduction was a threat not only to the oil industry, but to the entire economy of the state. The East Texas Chamber jumped into the fight in the face of bitter opposition and played a major part in molding sentiment for stabilization laws. Mr. Harrison, who served ten years as manager of the Wichita Falls Chamber of Commerce before coming to East Texas, will give some of the details of the successful campaign.

Mr. Harrison, I'm sure you recall the situation in the winter of 1930 and '31, when the first oil wells were brought in in the East Texas field. What was the attitude of the businessmen generally regarding control of oil production by law?

HARRISON: Well, I think it would be safe to say that at least ninety-five per cent of the citizens of East Texas were opposed to proration when the matter was first mentioned. Oil production was a new thing to East Texas. Most East Texans felt that a man had a right to do with his own property as he pleased and that he should be able to produce all the oil the well would make. It took a great deal of campaign work and educational work to make men realize that the owner of one well could not take out all of the oil it would produce without affecting surrounding oil property.

It was a long, hard battle and in the face of bitter opposition. I think that perhaps one reason that I was more concerned about proration and the control of the unrestricted production of oil was because I had served with oilmen and oil committees in the Wichita Falls Chamber of Commerce, and I knew something about the oil business in West Texas.

About the only allies that we had for proration or conservation were the timber men. The owners of timber land and the leaders in the lumber industry had already realized what conservation means in forestry. And it wasn't very much trouble to explain to them what conservation would mean in the oil industry. I remember that I brought up the subject of endorsing state proration laws three or four times in our board of directors without getting any action. One by one, some of our leaders began to see that it was a very serious situation, and that it affected not only the oil business, but that it would in time, if not controlled, ruin the great field that has meant so much to East Texas prosperity.

And so finally, in April 1931, at our annual convention at

Marlin, Guy Blount, who was our president that year, made a speech at the convention in which he endorsed proration, without any authority from our board of directors at the time. After our president had made a public declaration which was given wide publicity, our directors met and backed him up. And we threw all of our resources of our organization into the midst of the fight for proration.

HAYES: You remember, of course, when martial law was declared during the early days of the oil boom to keep down any possible violence?

HARRISON: I remember it very well. Of course, it must be recalled that at the time the East Texas oil field came in, we had no adequate proration laws in Texas. And all of that had to be worked out in the acts that the legislature passed, and then the statutes had to be tested out in the courts. And that took a long time. And while there was no law pertaining to the unrestricted production of oil, many people engaged in running what was commonly called "hot oil." That is oil over and above the allowable prescribed by the Railroad Commission.

During the time that the matter was being fought out in the courts, many men contended that there was no law on the subject. And many who were in debt, and who felt that they should get something out of their oil, proceeded to run it and sell it for whatever it would bring. Well, that brought about a situation that called for very unusual handling. It was in a way beyond the pale of the law; courts hadn't decided the question.

Governor Ross Sterling declared martial law, not only to keep down violence that might have resulted from disputes and fights in the oil field, but also to enforce the rulings of the Railroad Commission. Soldiers marched into the East Texas oil field, and it was an unusual and thrilling sight, something that very few people in East Texas had ever witnessed. There was no disorder, no violence towards the troops.

Most men saw that, for their good, for their own welfare as well as for the welfare of the industry, they should comply with the proration laws. Those who refused to do it were discovered one by one and finally were persuaded or forced to obey the regulations. Finally when court decisions upheld the statutes, then the federal authorities and the state authorities closed in on the hot-oil runners, and made it extremely unpopular.

During all of this period of pandemonium and confusion and lack of laws, the East Texas Chamber took the lead in fighting for proration and for orderly production of oil. Of course, I don't mean to imply that we were the only organization in this fight; there were many powerful trade groups, oil and gas associations, who had far more financial resources than we did and trained legal staffs who were working hard to bring order out of chaos. Numerous meetings were held of both factions. One faction wanted unrestricted production of oil, wanted every man to be able to handle his lease as he saw fit. Another group wanted strict enforcement of proration laws.

The big oil and gas associations were charged with special pleading and selfish interests when they advocated proration. Many people who didn't understand the situation thought that when the oil and gas associations got in the fight, it must be simply to protect some selfish interest of the oilmen. When we threw all of our resources into the fight on the side of proration, I believe that at that time it had a very great influence in tipping the scales of public opinion, and in influencing members of the legislature to pass the statutes that resulted finally in orderly production of oil.

HAYES: Would you hazard a guess as to what would have happened if proration laws hadn't been passed, and if unrestricted production had been allowed to continue—what would have happened to the business?

HARRISON: Well, I think by this time that the East Texas field would have been gutted completely. And that cities like Longview and Kilgore and Gladewater and Tyler, if they were not ghost towns, they certainly would have slipped back into the financial and business status of thirty years ago. Instead of that, we have literally thousands of people all over East Texas—and all over the United States for that matter—who are drawing monthly royalty checks from the East Texas oil field. East Texas was referred to as a backward and poverty-stricken area. Of course, since then, hundreds, maybe thousands, of men have become wealthy in this field. They've had money to invest in other enterprises, in new industries, and it has advanced the whole progress and economy not only of this region, but it's had its effect on all Texas.

I think too that the merchants in Dallas and Houston recognize that the East Texas oil field, coming as it did just at the time of the Great Depression, saved the lives of many a business institution in these great cities. Some Dallas and Houston businessmen recognized this and they have shown their appreciation by helping in development programs in our region.

HAYES: Mr. Harrison, what has the oil industry, do you think, done for the livestock industry and for agriculture and the development of other resources that otherwise would not have been developed?

HARRISON: Well, it has brought about a complete change in the agriculture and the livestock industry, and has brought a great improvement in rural housing. Many oilmen, or many men who have oil royalty income but whose background was that of farming and ranching, never had the money to buy purebred stock. They didn't have the money to build fine ranches or improve pastures. Since they have acquired some wealth through oil, many of them, hundreds, maybe thousands of them, have improved their farms, improved their ranches. They have been leaders in the pasture-improvement programs. They have bought fine registered bulls and have improved their herds. There are probably more fine beef and dairy cattle in East Texas today than in any other part of the state. And it is largely due to the fact that East Texas farmers and ranchmen and businessmen, who are interested in ranching on the side, have the surplus money to buy fine livestock. Some of the finest herds of cattle to be found in the whole United States are now in the East Texas region, fairly near the big East Texas oil field.

This extra income, that so many men have derived from oil, has gone back into soil conservation and improved housing and better fences, and has indirectly contributed to irrigation projects. The effect of the oil business and oil income on agriculture is so far-reaching that it's hard to describe it in detail.

HAYES: Thank you very much, Mr. Harrison. It's quite evident from what you say that East Texas, of which we're all so proud, would have been a vastly different place if the production of oil hadn't been controlled and your fight for proration had not been successful.

—*Hubert M. Harrison and R. M. Hayes*

Results of Conservation

I do believe that the old boom town is gone and our conservation has done that. We used to produce the oil and put it in tanks on top of the ground to evaporate and burn, just because there could be no cooperation among the oilmen and, too, we had no laws to help them. Was more everybody for himself, and there's always some holdout in any business, and almost as a matter of protection you had to produce the oil. In many cases, I suppose, a landowner could have made you produce the oil and store it in the tanks because his neighbor farmer was having his produced. I understand that started to a great extent in Pennsylvania where a judge likened oil to the capture of wild animals. He that got the oil first was the one that kept it. So I had read in books that that was kind of a precedent for the start of the race, and each one had to get all the oil out that he could first. In late years, with conservation laws where everyone has to obey them and produce a little more slowly and evenly, we're getting more oil out of the ground.

Even as a boy I used to read we weren't getting out over a fourth or a third of the oil. We recognized even as far back as my youth that we weren't getting all of the oil out, but we knew no other way to do it. Just open the wells up and let them flow, and as strange as it seems now, and as unbelievable as it seems, there was a prejudice among oilmen to shut a well in once it come in. They seemed to think that'd kill a well. I don't know why that could start when oil had been in the ground millions of years before we leased it. Why it shouldn't be back in again for a few days or a few weeks? Why would a few months kill the well and drive the oil away? We didn't have the good valves to hold the oil in and the good pipe fillings that we have now. It was almost a matter of having to let it go once we hit it, although we did keep gas wells shut in and could have oil just as easily. Now in later years, I'd say within the last twenty years, we have learned how to produce oil, and now I would say that we probably would get out two thirds of the oil—with one method of recovery that number would cover it as much as three fourths. I think the time will come when we get ninety per cent or more, as we learn more and more about that, more and more about secondary recovery.

—O. G. Lawson

Deep Drilling

When I first began drilling it cost around two thousand or three thousand dollars to drill a well. Pipe was forty cents a foot; now it's three dollars. And drill pipe, four-inch drill pipe, was forty cents, good heavy pipe, too, but we didn't have no tool joints. You had nothing except the collars like come on the pipe, and it would twist off. But now they got these tool joints—that was the biggest improvement. But we didn't have 'em till about 1912 and not many then. Now you can git all of 'em you want but they're expensive.

Some of those wells out in West Texas cost as much as five hundred thousand dollars. I've got a friend that run some big rigs out there, fellow used to roughneck for me back when. He's got some of those big rigs out there, that cost as much as five hundred thousand dollars. He told me that Gulf paid him over half a million dollars for drillin' one well. They drilled down to eight thousand feet, see, perpendicular. Put in a whipstock and diverted—say, forty-five-degree angle—and drilled five thousand or six thousand feet out south, then drilled in that same hole for five thousand or six thousand feet north, and then five thousand or six thousand feet west and then five thousand or six thousand feet east and the bottom of those holes would be a mile apart, more than a mile apart.

They'd test all that area out of one well, you see, like down in the Gulf there. Forty miles out the Magnolia built a concrete platform that's about three hundred foot square. They drilled a well straight down and then they drilled one on each corner horizontal, four more wells, five wells on that one little platform, about three hundred foot square. And they're doin' *everything* like that now. They have an engineer that sets there on the derrick and keeps tab on that log on the well, after they divert it horizontal. And they're doin' things like that. Looks like it'd just be impossible to an ordinary man. But these engineers are gettin' smarter than hell, I'll tell you. Nothing impossible now in the oil business. And these old drillers and engineers they've got out there have put a spark plug in this oil business. These big fellows, at the top, they don't know anything about the oil business any more. And they've made so damn much money they don't want to know. They just hire somebody that knows.

—*Clint Wood*

Directional Drilling

I've seen some wonderful fighting done by directional drilling, which is certainly a wonderful thing. I saw a big well up here north of Silsbee, in Hardin County, blow out and get away. And it cratered and made a tremendous crater there, and run for weeks. You could see it and hear it for twenty-five miles.

So the oil company that was interested there put up a drilling rig about twelve hundred feet from this well. And they drilled what you call a directional hole. This well as I remember was over eight thousand feet. So they drilled right down there and set casing in this directional hole, and they ran right into that pipe at the bottom. Then they pumped cement in the directional hole that they had drilled, and in that way they smothered the fire out. Then they went over in the crater and filled that old well up with cement. And then went back in the directional hole, and drilled that cement out and brought the well in. Now that's something that has developed in the last ten years in the oil business, and I think that's one of the greatest things that you'll see in drilling nowadays.

And that's all figured out by the engineers and the instruments that they have, and they can tell when they are in a fraction of an inch, about anything. Even about whether your well is out of line, or drilling over, off a piece of property, or whether it's absolutely perpendicular. I have known of wells being drilled under another man's property. That has occurred often. And, of course, if they can prove beyond a doubt, which they can nowadays with these instruments —why, they would have to reimburse this property owner for all this oil that they had extracted from out from under his land.

Of course, in the old days nobody could prove where the bottom of the hole was because the pipe, you know, is very flexible, and especially you get down to a depth of five or six or fifteen thousand feet—well, it's might near like handling a rope, see.

—W. C. Gilbert

Slumber Jay (ELECTRONIC LOGGING)

Jack Frazier was an early wildcatter, and in fact he was in my office here the other day [this recording was made July 22, 1953], talking about drilling a well again up in Hardin County. He drilled quite a few up there. In fact, the first Slumber Jay [Schlumberger] I ever saw in operation was on a well of his at Kountze years ago, when he had a big rig. And he told me to get up in the Slumber Jay truck van and watch 'em run it, and then go in the darkroom and watch them develop it. Then afterwards he and the Slumber Jay man explained to me the different markings on this paper, showing the different stratas of sand and water and shale and boulders and rock.

But this well was a dry hole so I didn't have the opportunity at that time to see how it looked with an oil sand.

Jack Frazier, as I remember him telling me once, he says, "Bill, I drilled fifty-nine dry holes, and 'course, that's financed mostly by the big companies and they had a small interest, and I was, of course, renting 'em my drilling rig for the operation. I remember drilling one over in the Hardin field north of Liberty, and I called the company that was interested and told 'em that I had gone to the depth that I had contracted to."

They said, "Well, Jack, have you Slumber Jayed the well?"

He said, "No, it cost too much money."

Says, "Well, before we pay you off you'll have to have it Slumber Jayed." And said he brought in a Slumber Jay and says while drilling the well he didn't see a thing, but after they Slumber Jayed it—why, they found an oil sand and set it in and made a producer.

—*W. C. Gilbert*

The Old Ways and the New

When I went to work for the Magnolia Petroleum Company in '27, we worked eighty-four hours a week. We worked seven twelve-hour days with an occasional day off once or twice a month. Today we're working forty hours a week, five eight-hour days. We have modern equipment. All of our wells are equipped with electric clocks where they start and shut themselves down.

It is interesting to think of the difference in oil-field work thirty-two years ago when I went to work and what it is today. Most of the work was done with shovels, teams, and wagons, and a few trucks. And it took lots of men and lots of man-hours to do the work that we can do in a few hours today. Our modern pulling units can get over the road much faster than they could in those days. They can rig up, pull a well, and be away before we could get rigged up good back in 1927.

The drilling operations have changed in proportion to the production. I'm in production, but when I went to work for the company I worked in the drilling department and it took us several days to get rigged up to go to work on the well and it was slow, but today the drilling units, they drill practically altogether with rotaries, and they are unitized where they can move in, raise their gin pole and go to drilling in a matter of hours.

—*Bruce Turner*

They hired anybody that could do a day's work in those days, and I never did know of a colored person going to work in the fields in Seminole or in this field either. I've known a few Indians that went to work, but about all they wanted back thirty years ago was somebody could just do a hard day's work. Somebody with a stiff back and a weak mind was all they were interested in. But today they are more selective in their hiring of men and the fact of the matter is, they don't hire too many. It's pretty hard now to get on with a major company for the simple reason that the modern equipment used doesn't require so many men and they have a lot of men that were hired back thirty years ago that are still with them and still operating this equipment. It's almost like getting an act through Congress to get on with one of these major companies. But when a person does get on with a major company, why he's almost a cinch to stay.

Back when I went to work for the company the oil business in Oklahoma was new and the early oil-field men that took the responsibility of developing these fields, most of them came from the Pennsylvania–West Virginia area, and now it's come to the place where there are not many West Virginians or men from Pennsylvania.

In 1927 pumpers drew a hundred and forty-five dollars a month. They worked by the month because that's the way they worked. They didn't work by the day. Twelve hours a day for every day, and they drew a hundred and forty-five dollars a month. And today those men are working forty hours a week, don't have as much hard work to do as they did then because kicking on those forty-horse Bessemers and Superiors wasn't always what it was supposed to be, but today they work forty hours with electric power. They get two dollars and seventy-five cents an hour for their work. They get eight holidays a year, where then, if they wanted us to have a holiday we got it, and if they didn't, we worked. [it.] But we get eight holidays now, and if it's necessary that we work on that holiday we get double time-and-a-half for it.

Thirty years ago [c. 1926] a lease of forty acres with four wells on it was considered a job for a pumper. He had his gas engines to look after and his ring fronts. That was considered a pretty good job. Some of them took care of as many as eight wells on an eighty [-acre tract], but when they got to more than that they doubled the job up and had more than one pumper. Today with this electric equipment, one pumper takes care of from fifteen to twenty-five wells for the simple reason that clocks automatically start and stop the wells. He doesn't have to go around every two or three hours and shut one down or start one up and maybe two or three hours later go back and shut it down. It's all done automatically and the principal thing now that a pumper has to do is just check his wells and see if they're pumping all right and see that they're not parted and keep the location cleaned up some, gauge his tanks, check his production. Now he can take care of several leases where then it was a man to every lease.

—*Bruce Turner*

Drillers and Roughnecks Today

The present-day worker in the oil fields is an entirely different chap. First of all, he's had the opportunity and availed himself of it. He's better educated. He's physically and mentally more alert and cleaner. And he's better trained—a good many of them with college educations or at least a high-school education with some vocational training in mechanics of some kind. The companies and the larger operators have become more cautious in their employment due to the imposition of a bunch of leeches claiming injuries and getting them a damage-suit lawyer. A back injury here and there and a few hernias that they had when they went to work for you.

They've gotten smarter. That is, smarter than they were. They still haven't gotten smart enough to beat it, but they're trying to cut down their percentage of losses in order to keep their insurance premiums within the bounds of reason so the ordinary operator can afford to pay it.

The companies now require a complete physical checkup, just about like going into the army, I imagine, almost as thorough and complete. If there's any physical imperfections or if they don't show up with good eyesight and mentally alert, they just can't go to work. And that's reducing the number of casualties. The other thing is that it's necessary for fellows to be better educated and better informed than we old-time well diggers were. A lot of us were pretty dumb, and you can't afford to be dumb now with one hundred fifty or two hundred fifty thousand dollars worth of fast rotary machinery and a lot of things around. Regardless of all the safety devices and safeguards and warnings and things that you can do for a fellow, he's still in some danger out there, and in order to operate the intricacies in the mechanism of the present-day machine, a fellow has to be smarter than the old boys I broke in with.

As a matter of fact, I doubt very seriously, even with the twenty-five or thirty years of drilling experience, whether I could walk out here and operate one of these present-day rigs. I don't think I know enough about them. I don't think I'd know what lever to pull or button to push. There's just too much machinery there for me. I can't run it.

The type and character of the men, in my judgment, in the aggregate—just a mean average of forty years' span—is vastly better. The work is lighter physically and much heavier mentally and much cleaner. I think the oil business is being run by a much brighter bunch of young fellows than I broke in with.

—Walter Cline

SIGNIFICANT
DATES
IN THE
HISTORY
OF THE
OIL
INDUSTRY

1846   Oil appears in salt well of father of Samuel Kier.

1847   Illuminating and lubricating oil made by James Young of Glasgow from petroleum spring in Colliery at Derbyshire. Spring yields three hundred gallons a day. When spring exhausted, Young and Meldrum make illuminant from coal, in 1851.

1849   Kier places rock oil on market as medicine.

1850   Kier distills petroleum to produce "carbon oil" for use in lamps.

1852   Luther and Withrow Atwood, Boston chemists, produce illuminating oil from coal tar.

1859 Oil struck in Drake well near Titusville, Pennsylvania, the first well drilled specifically for oil in the United States.

1860 First commercial oil well in West Virginia completed May 1.

First recorded production in Kentucky, Ohio.

1861 First cargo of oil exported to Europe.

First flowing well in Venango County, Pennsylvania.

First oil refinery on Oil Creek begins operation.

1865 Well completed on Pithole Creek, Pennsylvania, January 7. A town, Pithole City, grows up, reaching a population estimated as high as fifteen thousand in less than a year. In a few months it becomes a ghost town.

First successful pipe line completed. It is a two-inch line leading from Pithole, Pennsylvania, to the Miller farm, a distance of about five miles.

First shipment of oil in tank car made to New York in September. Two wooden tanks are mounted on a flat car.

1866 E. A. L. Roberts secures patent on method of increasing production by exploding "torpedo" at the bottom of the well.

1867 Oil used experimentally as fuel for steam locomotives, July 15.

1869 Joshua Merrill discovers process for de-odoring lubricants made from petroleum.

1870 First ocean-going vessel fitted for bulk shipment of oil.

Fifty-nine iron tanks provide a capacity of 794 tons.

1872 Natural gas piped to Titusville for domestic use.

1875 First commercial oil well in California.

1879 George B. Selden applies for patent on an automobile driven by an internal combustion engine.

A pipe line transporting oil from Bradford to Williamsport, Pennsylvania, a distance of 110 miles over the Allegheny Mountains, proves successful.

1880 Oil Exchange opens in Oil City, Pennsylvania, September 14.

1883 First oil well in Wyoming completed.

1889   First commercial production in Illinois.

       First gasoline-powered tractor put to work on farm.

1892   First commercial production in Kansas.

1893   First movement of refined oil by pipe line. Kerosene is pumped from the Pennsylvania fields to Wilkes-Barre, a distance of 252 miles.

       Charles Duryea of Springfield, Massachusetts, mounts one-cylinder gasoline engine in buggy to produce first gasoline-propelled automobile in the United States. (Horseless carriage had been propelled by steam and electricity.)

1894   Oil struck at Corsicana in a well being drilled for water.

1897   First commercial oil well in Oklahoma brought in at Bartlesville.

       The Rio Bravo Oil Company, a subsidiary of the Southern Pacific Railroad, becomes the first oil company to set up a geological department.

       First diesel engine built in the United States.

1898   Refinery at Corsicana goes into operation on Christmas Day.

1900   Eight thousand automobiles registered in the United States. First automobile show in the United States held in New York City, November 3–10.

1901   The Lucas Gusher, the largest producer yet drilled, comes in near Beaumont, Texas, January 10.

       14,800 automobiles registered in the United States.

       First producing oil well in Louisiana completed September 21.

1902   Gasoline tractors on market.

1903   First transcontinental automobile trip made from San Francisco to New York, May 23 to August 1.

       Ford Motor Company organized.

       Orville Wright makes first airplane flight, December 17.

1904   The United States Navy tests oil as fuel for torpedo boats.

1905   First garage opened.

1906   Eleven companies begin manufacture of farm tractors powered by internal combustion engines.

1908 Ford Model T placed in production.

1909 Hughes rock bit for use in rotary drilling goes into production.

1910 Gusher brought in near Maricopa, California.

1912 First automobile (Cadillac) to come equipped with self-starter. More and more women will be driving cars.

Cushing field discovered in Oklahoma.

1913 William M. Burton secures patent on cracking process, whereby a larger yield of gasoline per barrel of oil is produced.

Ford factory establishes assembly line and cuts price of cars.

First major production in Mexico.

1914 First commercial oil production in Montana.

Voluntary proration established in the Cushing field in Oklahoma.

Construction begins on transcontinental highway.

1915 Patent issued for Dubbs cracking process—distillation under self-generated pressure.

1916 First act of Congress providing federal aid for the construction of roads.

1919 Practical oil burner for central home heating developed.

First production in Arkansas.

1921 Anti-knock properties of tetraethyl lead discovered.

1923 "Ethyl" gasoline placed on the market.

1925 First diesel-electric locomotive placed in service.

1926 Everette L. DeGoyler discovers oil in Fort Bend County, Texas, by use of geophysical methods.

1927 Hobbs field in New Mexico discovered.

1930 Construction begins on first multiproduct long-distance pipe line from Borger, Texas, to East St. Louis, Illinois, later extended to East Chicago, Indiana.

Great East Texas field opened by discovery in Rusk County.

1932 Federal sales tax on gasoline goes into effect.

1935 Interstate Oil Compact Commission signed by representatives of six oil-producing states.

1936   Water flooding used for secondary recovery of oil at Burk-burnett field in Texas.

1937   First commercial catalytic cracking plant placed in operation at Marcus Hook, Pennsylvania.

First patent for butyl rubber issued.

1941   Seventy-eight leaders from all branches of the oil industry are appointed to the Petroleum Industry Council for National Defense by Petroleum Coordinator Harold Ickes.

1942   The Petroleum Administration for War appointed by President Roosevelt, with Harold Ickes as Petroleum Administrator.

Petroleum begins flowing into the "Big Inch" pipe line extending from Longview, Texas, to Norris City, Illinois. The purpose of this line is to avoid exposing coastal tankers to German submarines. The line is later extended to New York City.

1944   Products begin flowing through the "Little Big Inch" pipe line from Houston, Texas, to Linden, New Jersey.

Normandy invasion launched June 6; pipe line laid across the English Channel.

1945   First offshore lease sale held by state of Louisiana.

1951   Discovery well in the United States portion of Williston Basin in North Dakota completed.

A
SELECTED
BIBLIOGRAPHY

GENERAL WORKS

American Petroleum Quarterly, Centennial Issue, New York, 1959.

Ball, Max Waite, *This Fascinating Oil Business*, New York, 1940.

Bone, J. H. A., *Petroleum and Petroleum Wells*, Philadelphia, 1865.

Clark, J. Stanley, *The Oil Century—from the Drake Well to the Conservation Era*, Norman, 1958.

Clark, James A., and Halbouty, Michael T., *Spindletop*, New York, 1952.

Fanning, Leonard M., *The Rise of American Oil*, New York, 1948.

Forbes, Gerald, *Flush Production*, Norman, 1942.

Giddens, Paul Henry, *The Birth of the Oil Industry*, New York, 1938.

——, *Early Days of Oil*, Princeton, 1948.

Glasscock, C. B., *Then Oil Came*, Indianapolis, 1938.

Knowles, Ruth Sheldon, *The Greatest Gamblers*, New York, 1959.

Rister, Carl Coke, *Oil! Titan of the Southwest*, Norman, 1949.

Tait, Samuel W., Jr., *The Wild Catters*, Princeton, 1946.

FOLKLORE

Boatright, Mody C., *Folklore of the Oil Industry*, Dallas, 1963.

——, and Morgan, Gib, *Minstrel of the Oil Field*, Austin, 1945.

COMPANY HISTORIES

Beaton, Kendall, *Enterprise in Oil: A History of Shell in the United States*, New York, 1957.

Gibbs, George Sweet, and Knowlton, Evelyn H., *The Resurgent Years (History of the Standard Oil Company of New Jersey)*, New York, 1956.

Giddens, Paul Henry, *Standard Oil Company (Indiana): Oil Pioneer of the Middle West*, New York, 1955.

Hidy, Ralph Willard, and Hidy, Muriel E., *Pioneering in Big Business, 1882–1911 (History of the Standard Oil Company of New Jersey)*, New York, 1955.

James, Marquis, *The Texaco Story—The First Fifty Years, 1902–1952*, New York, 1953.

Larson, Henrietta M., and Parter, Kenneth W., *History of the Humble Oil and Refining Company*, New York, 1959.

Welty, Earl M., and Taylor, Frank J., *The Black Bonanza (History of the Union Oil Company of California)*, New York, 1956.

INDEX

A

H